Something Big Has Been Here

Something BIG

...las Been Here

poems by JACK PRELUTSKY

drawings by JAMES STEVENSON

Greenwillow Books, New York

Greenwillow Books

To children's booksellers everywhere

Something Big Has Been Here

Something big has been here,
what it was, I do not know,
for I did not see it coming,
and I did not see it go,
but I hope I never meet it,
if I do, I'm in a fix,
for it left behind its footprints,
they are size nine-fifty-six.

An Early Worm Got out of Bed

An early worm got out of bed
and murmured, "I feel mean!
I'll put my darkest glasses on,
I'll paint myself bright green.

"I'll dress up in my wildest wig,
the one with purple bangs,
I'll also wear a pair of horns
and artificial fangs."

That early worm poked up its head,
which looked a perfect fright,
an early bird observed that worm
and lost its appetite.

I Know All the Sounds that the Animals Make

I know all the sounds that the animals make,
and make them all day from the moment I wake,
I roar like a mouse and I purr like a moose,
I hoot like a duck and I moo like a goose.

I squeak like a cat and I quack like a frog,
I oink like a bear and I honk like a hog,
I croak like a cow and I bark like a bee,
no wonder the animals marvel at me.

9

Happy Birthday, Mother Dearest

Happy birthday, Mother dearest,
we made breakfast just for you,
a watermelon omelette,
and a dish of popcorn too,
a cup of milk and sugar,
and a slice of blackened toast,
happy birthday, Mother dearest,
you're the one we love the most.

We're Four Ferocious Tigers

We're four ferocious tigers,
at least, that's what we seem,
our claws are at the ready,
our sharp incisors gleam,
we're quite intimidating,
our stare will make you blink,
our roar will make you shiver,
at least, that's what we think.

We're four ferocious tigers,
at least, that's what we hear,
our ominous demeanor
will chill your atmosphere,
and yet you need not fear us,
don't scream and run away,
we only eat spaghetti,
at least, that's what we say.

11

I Am Growing a Glorious Garden

I am growing a glorious garden,
resplendent with trumpets and flutes,
I am pruning euphonium bushes,
I am watering piccolo shoots,
my tubas and tambourines flourish,
surrounded by saxophone reeds,
I am planting trombones and pianos,
and sowing sweet sousaphone seeds.

12

I have cymbals galore in my garden,
staid oboes in orderly rows,
there are flowering fifes and violas
in the glade where the glockenspiel grows,
there are gongs and guitars in abundance,
there are violins high on the vine,
and an arbor of harps by the bower
where the cellos and clarinets twine.

My bassoons are beginning to blossom,
as my zithers and mandolins bloom,
my castanets happily chatter,
my kettledrums merrily boom,
the banjos that branch by the bugles
play counterpoint with a kazoo,
come visit my glorious garden
and hear it play music for you.

As Soon as Fred Gets out of Bed

As soon as Fred gets out of bed,
his underwear goes on his head.
His mother laughs, "Don't put it there,
a head's no place for underwear!"
But near his ears, above his brains,
is where Fred's underwear remains.

At night when Fred goes back to bed,
he deftly plucks it off his head.
His mother switches off the light
and softly croons, "Good night! Good night!"
And then, for reasons no one knows,
Fred's underwear goes on his toes.

Belinda Blue

Belinda Blue was furious,
she fumed, "I'm really mad!
This is the worst experience
that I have ever had."
She beat her fists against the wall,
she pounded on the floor,
"I am livid!" she exploded,
"I am bilious to the core!"

She wrung her hands, she tore her hair,
her tantrum grew and grew,
"I am angry, **angry, ANGRY!**"
shrieked enraged Belinda Blue.
She seemed to be beside herself,
she raced around the room,
she roared so loud, the neighbors thought
they'd heard a sonic boom.

Her rage was unabated,
it appeared she'd never quit,
in fact, she seemed to savor
every second of her fit,
Belinda Blue created
such an overwhelming scene
because at lunch, her mother said,
"Please eat just one green bean."

The Turkey Shot out of the Oven

The turkey shot out of the oven
and rocketed into the air,
it knocked every plate off the table
and partly demolished a chair.

It ricocheted into a corner
and burst with a deafening boom,
then splattered all over the kitchen,
completely obscuring the room.

It stuck to the walls and the windows,
it totally coated the floor,
there was turkey attached to the ceiling,
where there'd never been turkey before.

It blanketed every appliance,
it smeared every saucer and bowl,
there wasn't a way I could stop it,
that turkey was out of control.

I scraped and I scrubbed with displeasure,
and thought with chagrin as I mopped,
that I'd never again stuff a turkey
with popcorn that hadn't been popped.

I Am Wunk

I am Wunk, a wacky wizard,
and I wield a willow wand.
I wave it once, and there you swim,
a minnow in a pond.
I wave it twice, and there you sit,
a lizard on a log.
I wave it thrice, and there you fly,
a fly before a frog.

I am Wunk, a wily wizard,
and I hold a crystal sphere.
I spin it with my fingers,
you've a carrot in your ear.
I roll it on the table,
you've an anvil on your head.
I place it on your pillow,
you've a lion in your bed.

I am Wunk, a wondrous wizard,
and I wear a woolen hat.
I take it off and fold it,
you are smaller than a cat.
I put it in my pocket,
you are smaller than a mouse.
Do be quick, your doorbell's ringing . . .
I am Wunk outside your house.

Denson Dumm

Denson Dumm, with pomp and flair,
planted lightbulbs in his hair.
Now, however dark the night,
Denson Dumm is always bright.

You're Eating Like a Pig Again!

"You're eating like a pig again!"
my mother scolded me,
"If you keep eating like a pig,
a pig is what you'll be!"

I simply cannot fathom
what the fuss is all about,
and haven't I a lovely tail,
and see my splendid snout.

I Am Tired of Being Little

I am tired of being little,
I am sick of being thin,
I wish that I were giant size,
with whiskers on my chin.
No one would dare to tease me,
or to take away my toys,
for I would be much bigger
than the biggest bigger boys.

My folks would pay attention
to everything I said,
they couldn't make me eat my peas
or tell me, "Go to bed!"
I'd never be afraid again
if I were ten-foot-three,
I wish that I were giant size,
instead of small like me.

You're Nasty and You're Loud

You're nasty and you're loud,
you're mean enough for two.
If I could be a cloud,
I'd rain all day on you.

They Tell Me I'm Peculiar

They tell me I'm peculiar,
they seem to think I'm odd,
they look at me and grimace,
I smile at them and nod.

They cringe at my behavior,
"Unthinkable!" they say,
they're shocked that I love liver
and eat it every day.

I Should Have Stayed in Bed Today

I should have stayed in bed today,
in bed's where I belong,
as soon as I got up today,
things started going wrong,
I got a splinter in my foot,
my puppy made me fall,
I squirted toothpaste in my ear,
I crashed into the wall.

I knocked my homework off the desk,
it landed on my toes,
I spilled a glass of chocolate milk,
it's soaking through my clothes,
I accidentally bit my tongue,
that really made me moan,
and it was far from funny
when I banged my funny bone.

I scraped my knees, I bumped my nose,
I sat upon a pin,
I leapt up with alacrity,
and sharply barked my shin,
I stuck a finger in my eye,
the pain is quite severe,
I'd better get right back to bed
and stay there for a year.

Kevin the King of the Jungle

I'm Kevin the king of the jungle,
I live at the top of a tree,
although I behave like a monkey,
no lion is braver than me,
I swing through the air with abandon,
laughing a simian laugh,
I'm strong as my uncle gorilla,
I'm swift as my cousin giraffe.

I wrestle with dozens of gibbons,
I win, but they don't seem to mind,
I race with gazelles and impalas,
and frequently leave them behind,
hyenas and rhinos obey me,
great elephants do what I say,
and when I jump into the river,
fierce crocodiles hurry away.

I'm Kevin the king of the jungle,
I'm agile, I'm crafty, I'm bold,
green leaves are my only apparel,
and yet I have never caught cold,
my stepmother was a chimpanzee,
my stepfather was a baboon,
and that's why I eat with my fingers
instead of a fork or a spoon.

If I see a hippo look hungry,
I share a few edible roots,
when zebras or ostriches quarrel,
I settle their family disputes,
I'm Kevin the king of the jungle,
the lord of the leopard and gnu,
feel free to drop by my dominion,
I'll peel a banana for you.

Little Bird Outside My Window

Little bird outside my window,
I can hear you in my room
as you gaily serenade me
and eradicate the gloom.

Your chirping is the sweetest
that my ears have ever heard,
it awakens me each morning—
zip your beak up, little bird!

Unhappy South Pole Penguin

Unhappy South Pole penguin,
you are in a nasty mood
as you try to chew your dinner
which refuses to be chewed,
but a simple undertaking
will improve your attitude. . . .
you must first defrost your dinner,
for your dinner's frozen food.

Watson Watts

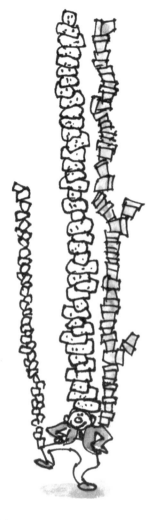

Watson Watts, atop his head,
balanced forty loaves of bread.
Forty loaves! no less, no more—
not one crumb fell to the floor.

On his shoulders, Watson Watts
balanced forty flowerpots.
Forty pots! no more, no less—
yet he met with great success.

34

Watson balanced on his knees
forty chunks of Cheddar cheese.
Forty chunks! no less, no more—
just like loaves and pots before.

Watson Watts, upon his legs,
balanced forty ostrich eggs.
Forty eggs! no more, no less—
it took months to clean the mess!

Hello! How Are You? I Am Fine!

Hello! How are you? I am fine!
is all my dog will say,
he's probably repeated it
a thousand times today.
He doesn't bark his normal bark,
he doesn't even whine,
he only drones the same **Hello!**
How are you? I am fine!

Hello! How are you? I am fine!
his message doesn't change,
it's gotten quite monotonous,
and just a trifle strange.
Hello! How are you? I am fine!
it makes the neighbors stare,
they're unaware that yesterday
he ate my talking bear.

Life's Not Been the Same in My Family

Life's not been the same in my family
since the day that the new baby came,
my parents completely ignore me,
they scarcely remember my name.

The baby gets all their attention,
"Oh, isn't she precious!" they croon,
they think that she looks like an angel,
I think she resembles a prune.

They're thrilled when she giggles or gurgles,
"She burped!" they exclaim with delight,
they don't even mind when she wakes us
with deafening screams in the night.

They seem to believe she's a treasure,
there's simply no way I agree,
I wish she'd stop being a baby
and start being older than me.

I Met a Rat of Culture

I met a rat of culture
who was elegantly dressed
in a pair of velvet trousers
and a silver-buttoned vest,
he related ancient proverbs
and recited poetry,
he spoke a dozen languages,
eleven more than me.

That rat was perspicacious,
and had cogent things to say
on bionics, economics,
hydroponics, and ballet,
he instructed me in sculpture,
he shed light on keeping bees,
then he painted an acrylic
of an abstract view of cheese.

He had circled the equator,
he had visited the poles,
he extolled the art of sailing
while he baked assorted rolls,
he wove a woolen carpet
and he shaped a porcelain pot,
then he sang an operetta
while he danced a slow gavotte.

He was versed in aviation,
an authority on trains,
all of botany and baseball
were contained within his brains,
he knew chemistry and physics,
he had taught himself to sew,
to my knowledge, there was nothing
that the rodent did not know.

He was vastly more accomplished
than the billions of his kin,
he performed a brief sonata
on a tiny violin,
but he squealed and promptly vanished
at the entrance of my cat,
for despite his erudition,
he was nothing but a rat.

Do Not Disturb the Woolly Wurbbe

Do not disturb the woolly Wurbbe
that scarcely seems to stir,
but sits upon the corner curb
and combs its curly fur.

There's nowhere that it cares to go,
it calmly stays in place
and grooms itself from head to toe,
contentment on its face.

To park upon that paving stone
is all it wants to do,
and if you leave the Wurbbe alone,
it will not bother you.

My Neighbor's Dog Is Purple

My neighbor's dog is purple,
its eyes are large and green,
its tail is almost endless,
the longest I have seen.

My neighbor's dog is quiet,
it does not bark one bit,
but when my neighbor's dog is near,
I feel afraid of it.

My neighbor's dog looks nasty,
it has a wicked smile. . . .
before my neighbor painted it,
it was a crocodile.

I Am a Ghost Who's Lost His Boo

I am a ghost who's lost his boo,
my boo is gone from me,
and I'm without a single clue
to where my boo might be.
It makes me mope, it makes me pout,
it almost makes me moan,
a ghost is not a ghost without
a boo to call his own.

My boo was piercing, fierce, and loud,
I used to strut and boast,
for I was positively proud
to be a gruesome ghost.
But now that I'm without a boo,
I find it rather weird,
there's little for a ghost to do
whose boo has disappeared.

Although I hover here and there,
and haunt a hundred rooms,
it seems there's no one I can scare
unless my boo resumes.
I am a ghost who's lost his boo,
alas! A boo I lack,
if you should find my boo, then you
had better give it back.

Last Night I Dreamed of Chickens

Last night I dreamed of chickens,
there were chickens everywhere,
they were standing on my stomach,
they were nesting in my hair,
they were pecking at my pillow,
they were hopping on my head,
they were ruffling up their feathers
as they raced about my bed.

They were on the chairs and tables,
they were on the chandeliers,
they were roosting in the corners,
they were clucking in my ears,
there were chickens, chickens, chickens
for as far as I could see. . . .
when I woke today, I noticed
there were eggs on top of me.

My Brother Built a Robot

My brother built a robot
that does not exactly work,
as soon as it was finished,
it began to go berserk,
its eyes grew incandescent
and its nose appeared to gleam,
it bellowed unbenignly
and its ears emitted steam.

My brother built that robot
to help us clean our room,
instead, it ate the dust pan
and attacked us with the broom,
it pulled apart our pillows,
it disheveled both our beds,
it took a box of crayons
and it doodled on our heads.

That robot seemed relentless
as it tied our socks in knots,
then clunked into the kitchen
and dismantled pans and pots,
the thing was not behaving
in the fashion we had planned,
it clanked into the bathroom
and it filled the tub with sand.

We tried to disconnect it,
but it was to no avail,
it picked us up and dropped us
in an empty garbage pail,
we cannot stop that robot,
for we're stymied by one hitch. . . .
my brother didn't bother
to equip it with a switch.

An Auk in Flight

An auk in flight
is sheer delight,
it soars above the sea.

An auk on land
is not so grand—
an auk walks **auk**wardly.

Fenton Phlantz

Fenton Phlantz is fairly weird,
he puts peanuts in his beard,
elephants are often found
following Fenton Phlantz around.

My Uncle Looked Me in the Eye

My uncle looked me in the eye
about an hour ago,
he said, "There are some things I think
that you had better know—
do not throw bricks at bumblebees
or grab a grizzly bear,
and never tug a tiger's tail
or pull a panther's hair.

"Don't wrestle with a rattlesnake
or ask a skunk to fight,
don't irritate an elephant
or tempt a lion to bite,
don't scuffle with a buffalo
or tease electric eels,
don't interrupt piranhas
at their underwater meals.

"Don't tickle a gorilla
    or invite a shark to smile,
    don't hug a hippopotamus
    or kiss a crocodile,
    don't ridicule a rhino
    or provoke a porcupine."
    I've followed his advice so far,
    and I am doing fine.

Grasshopper Gumbo

GRASSHOPPER GUMBO

IGUANA TAIL TARTS

TOAD À LA MODE

PICKLED PELICAN PARTS

ELEPHANT GELATIN

FROG FRICASSEE

PURÉE OF PLATYPUS

BOILED BUMBLEBEE

PORCUPINE PUDDING

STEAMED CENTIPEDE SKINS

SQUID SUCKER SUNDAES

FRIED FLYING FISH FINS

MEADOW MOUSE MORSELS

CRACKED CROCODILE CRUNCH

The school cafeteria
serves them for lunch.

52

The Rains in Little Dribbles

The rains in Little Dribbles
are the sort one rarely sees,
every Thursday it pours cola,
Friday showers herbal teas,
early Saturday a sprinkle
of sweet cider fills the air,
then on Sunday sarsaparilla
soaks the citizenry there.

Monday morning, mocha malteds
softly saturate the town,
while on Tuesday lemon droplets
drizzle delicately down,
but the rain that rains on Wednesday
is a watermelon tide,
so the folks in Little Dribbles
spend their Wednesdays safe inside.

Today I Shall Powder My Elephant's Ears

Today I shall powder my elephant's ears
and paint his posterior red,
I'll trim all his toenails with suitable shears
and place a toupee on his head.

Tonight I shall tie a balloon to his tail
and wrap him in feathers and furs,
then fasten his necktie and velveteen veil
and put on his boots and his spurs.

54

There'll be a warm smile on my elephant's face
as we're welcomed to Pachyderm Hall,
to dance until daybreak with elegant grace
at the elephants' masquerade ball.

A Remarkable Adventure

I was at my bedroom table
with a notebook open wide,
when a giant anaconda
started winding up my side,
I was filled with apprehension
and retreated down the stairs,
to be greeted at the bottom
by a dozen grizzly bears.

We tumultuously tussled
till I managed to get free,
then I saw, with trepidation,
there were tigers after me,
I could feel them growing closer,
I was quivering with fear,
then I blundered into quicksand
and began to disappear.

I was rescued by an eagle
that descended from the skies
to embrace me with its talons,
to my terror and surprise,
but that raptor lost its purchase
when a blizzard made me sneeze,
and it dropped me in a thicket
where I battered both my knees.

I was suddenly surrounded
by a troop of savage trolls,
who maliciously informed me
they would toast me over coals,
I was lucky to elude them
when they briefly looked away—
that's the reason why my homework
isn't here with me today.

Squirrels

Squirrels, often found in parks,
have tails resembling question marks.
It's just coincidental, though. . . .
there's little squirrels care to know.

Katy Ate a Baked Potato

Katy ate a baked potato, strolling through the mews
in her yellow elevator alligator shoes.
That was Katy's last potato, she did not survive—
her elevator alligator shoes were still alive.

The Addle-pated Paddlepuss

The Addle-pated Paddlepuss
is agile as a cat,
its neck is long and limber,
and its face is broad and flat,
it moves with skill and vigor,
with velocity and grace,
as it spends its every second
playing Ping-Pong with its face.

The Addle-pated Paddlepuss
prevails in every game,
its opponent doesn't matter,
the result is all the same,
with its supersonic smashes
and its convoluted spins,
it demolishes all comers
and invariably wins.

The Addle-pated Paddlepuss,
with effervescent verve,
follows innovative volleys
with a scintillating serve,
if you're fond of playing Ping-Pong
and would like to lose in style,
the Addle-pated Paddlepuss
will serve you for awhile.

The Zoo Was in an Uproar

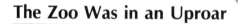

The zoo was in an uproar,
the rabbits stamped their feet,
the pigs expressed displeasure,
the gnus refused to eat,
"Disgraceful!" gabbed the gibbons,
"Barbaric!" boomed a bear,
"Distressing!" wept a leopard,
the ferrets fumed, *"Unfair!"*

"Repellant!" puled a puma,
"Bizarre!" a badger bawled,
　the donkeys were disgusted,
　the pandas were appalled,
　the camels ran for cover,
　a turtle fled her shell,
　the seals stayed underwater,
　a walrus felt unwell.

"How wicked!" whined a weasel,
"Uncalled for!" cawed the crows,
　the tigers lost their tempers,
　a polecat held his nose,
"Unseemly!" screamed the eagles,
　the lions roared with wrath,
　that day the hippopotamus
　forgot to take a bath.

63

Twaddletalk Tuck

I'm Twaddletalk Tuck and I talk and I talk
and I talk when I run and I talk when I walk
and I talk when I hop and I talk when I creep
and I talk when I wake and I talk when I sleep
and I talk when it's wet and I talk when it's dry
and I talk when I laugh and I talk when I cry
and I talk when I jump and I talk when I land
and I talk when I sit and I talk when I stand
and I talk and I talk into anyone's ear
and I talk and I talk when there's nobody near
and I talk when I'm hoarse and my voice is a squawk
for I'm Twaddletalk Tuck and I talk and I talk.

Slow Sloth's Slow Song

I . . . . *am* . . . . . . *a* . . . . . . *sloth* . . . . . .
a . . . . . . *sloth* . . . . . . *am* . . . . . . *I* . . . . . .
I . . . . . . *live* . . . . . . *in* . . . . . . *trees* . . . . . .
But . . . . . . *I* . . . . . . *can't* . . . . . . *fly* . . . . . .
I . . . . . . *do* . . . . . . *not* . . . . . . *run* . . . . . .
I . . . . . . *am* . . . . . . *so* . . . . . . *slow* . . . . . .
But . . . . . . *I* . . . . . . *am* . . . . . . *where* . . . . . .
I . . . . . . *want* . . . . . . *to* . . . . . . *go* .

My Mother Made a Meat Loaf

My mother made a meat loaf
that provided much distress,
she tried her best to serve it,
but she met with no success,
her sharpest knife was powerless
to cut a single slice,
and her efforts with a cleaver
failed completely to suffice.

She whacked it with a hammer,
and she smacked it with a brick,
but she couldn't faze that meat loaf,
it remained without a nick,
I decided I would help her
and assailed it with a drill,
but the drill made no impression,
though I worked with all my skill.

We chipped at it with chisels,
but we didn't make a dent,
it appeared my mother's meat loaf
was much harder than cement,
then we set upon that meat loaf
with a hatchet and an ax,
but that meat loaf stayed unblemished
and withstood our fierce attacks.

We borrowed bows and arrows,
and we fired at close range,
it didn't make a difference,
for that meat loaf didn't change,
we beset it with a blowtorch,
but we couldn't find a flaw,
and we both were flabbergasted
when it broke the power saw.

We hired a hippopotamus
to trample it around,
but that meat loaf was so mighty
that it simply stood its ground,
now we manufacture meat loaves
by the millions, all year long,
they are famous in construction,
building houses tall and strong.

We're Know-nothing Neebies

We're Know-nothing Neebies
with nothing to say,
and certain to say it
without a delay,
we're perfectly pompous,
indelibly dense,
we haven't a trace
of a semblance of sense.

We're Know-nothing Neebies,
complacent and proud,
the things we don't know
we proclaim very loud,
from summer to winter,
from spring until fall,
we daily display
we know nothing at all.

We're Know-nothing Neebies,
invincibly vain,
distinguished by pates
with no space for a brain,
you cannot avoid us,
we've never been rare,
just look all around you,
we're found everywhere.

Who Pulled the Plug in My Ant Farm?

Who pulled the plug in my ant farm?
Who let my ants get away?
Their tunnels are almost deserted,
I'm having a miserable day.
They've gathered in groups in the corners,
they're swarming all over the floor,
for each one I get in my clutches,
there seem to be two dozen more.

I'm doing my best to corral them,
I doubt that I'll ever be done,
there's nothing as hard to recapture
as hundreds of ants on the run.
My mother found ants in her slippers,
my sister found ants in her shoes,
they got in my father's pajamas,
he bellowed, "I'm blowing a fuse!"

Some have invaded the kitchen,
they've started attacking our food,
my mother is shrieking in horror,
and I'm in a horrible mood.
Who pulled the plug in my ant farm,
infesting our home with those pests?
I have the unhappy suspicion
that ants are our permanent guests.

Today I'm Going Yesterday

Today I'm going yesterday
as quickly as I can,
I'm confident I'll do it,
I've devised a clever plan,
it involves my running backward
at a constant rate of speed,
if I'm mindful of my timing,
I'll undoubtedly succeed.

Today I'm going yesterday,
I'm moving very fast
as I'm putting off the future
for the rather recent past,
I can feel the present fading
as I hastily depart,
and look forward to arriving
on the day before I start.

Today I'm going yesterday,
I'm slipping out of sight
and anticipate I'll vanish
just a bit before tonight,
when I reach my destination,
I'll compose a note to say
that I'll see you all tomorrow,
which of course will be today.

There's No One as Slow as Slomona

There's no one as slow as Slomona,
Slomona's unbearably slow,
it takes her as long to eat breakfast
as it takes a tomato to grow,
she sits in the kitchen all morning
and nibbles a morsel of bread,
she dawdles so long at the table,
it's time to get ready for bed.

There's no one as slow as Slomona,
her pace makes molasses seem fast,
she once raced a snail and a turtle
and finished a definite last,
she never does anything quickly,
but inches along at a crawl,
one winter she sat on a splinter
and didn't shout "Ouch!" until fall.

Don't Yell at Me!

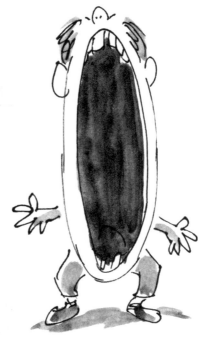

Don't yell at me!
Don't yell at me!
I hate it when you do,
it makes me feel so miserable,
I want to run from you.
I simply cannot stand it
when you scream into my ear,
if I knew how to do it,
I'd completely disappear.

Don't yell at me!
Don't yell at me!
I'll crawl away and hide,
I'll detonate to smithereens
or shrivel up inside.
Feel free to thumb your nose at me,
or wiggle all your toes at me,
or even ring a bell at me,
but please, **please, please,**
DON'T YELL AT ME!

75

Nigel Gline

When Nigel Gline sat down to dine,
he yawned, "This meal's a bore!
It's nothing more than what I've had
a thousand times before.
I'm through with cheese and chocolate,
I'm done with beans and beef,
I'd like a tasty tree instead."
So Nigel ate a leaf.

He liked that leaf, and swallowed more,
then nibbled on a twig,
that hardly seemed to be enough,
his appetite was big,
the twigs were so delicious
that he started on a limb,
soon every branch upon that tree
had vanished into him.

"It's time to try the trunk!" he said,
and ate it on the spot,
the bark was easy to digest,
the knots, of course, were not.
Now Nigel Gline declines to dine,
deep roots grow from his toes,
and birds nest in the leafy boughs
that stem from Nigel's nose.

They Never Send Sam to the Store Anymore

The day they sent Sam to the grocery store
to purchase a carton of eggs,
he brought back a pear with a pearl in its core,
and a leopard with lavender legs.

He returned with an elephant small as a mouse,
a baseball that bounces a mile,
a little tame dragon that heats up the house,
and a lantern that lights when they smile.

Sam brought them a snowball that never feels cold,
a gossamer carpet that flies,
a salmon of silver, a grackle of gold,
and an ermine with emerald eyes.

They never send Sam to the store anymore,
no matter how often he begs,
for he brought back a dodo that danced on the floor,
but he didn't bring home any eggs.

I Wave Good-bye When Butter Flies

I wave good-bye when butter flies
and cheer a boxing match,
I've often watched my pillow fight,
I've sewn a cabbage patch,
I like to dance at basket balls
or lead a rubber band,
I've marvelled at a spelling bee,
I've helped a peanut stand.

It's possible a pencil points,
but does a lemon drop?
Does coffee break or chocolate kiss,
and will a soda pop?
I share my milk with drinking straws,
my meals with chewing gum,
and should I see my pocket change,
I'll hear my kettle drum.

It makes me sad when lettuce leaves,
I laugh when dinner rolls,
I wonder if the kitchen sinks
and if a salad bowls,
I've listened to a diamond ring,
I've waved a football fan,
and if a chimney sweeps the floor,
I'm sure the garbage can.

My Frog Is a Frog

My frog is a frog that is hopelessly hoarse,
my frog is a frog with a reason, of course,
my frog is a frog that cannot croak a note,
my frog is a frog with a frog in its throat.

Wilhelmina Wafflewitz

I'm Wilhelmina Wafflewitz,
I never can decide
the things I think I'd like to do,
although I think I've tried.
What should I wear? When should I eat?
Where do I want to go?
Should I do this, or that instead?
I never seem to know.

I'm Wilhelmina Wafflewitz,
and I'm afraid I find
it practically impossible
to know what's on my mind.
Since I'm unsure of what to do,
I think I'll stay quite still,
at least, I think, I think I think,
I think I think I will.

I'm Off to Catch a Bumblebee

I'm off to catch a bumblebee,
so bumblebees beware!
I've brought the best equipment,
with accessories to spare—
a bottle full of buttons
and a carton full of corks,
assorted socks and saucers
and a gross of broken forks.

I'm off to catch a bumblebee,
I'll surely find one soon,
I've got a pound of pepper
and a helium balloon,
my trusty feather duster
and eleven bars of soap,
a pair of pop-up toasters
and a leaky periscope.

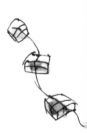

I have brought my beach umbrella,
I have brought my Hula Hoop,
my yo-yo and viola
and a bowl of chicken soup,
a lariat that's large enough
to loop about a bear—
I'm off to catch a bumblebee,
so bumblebees beware!

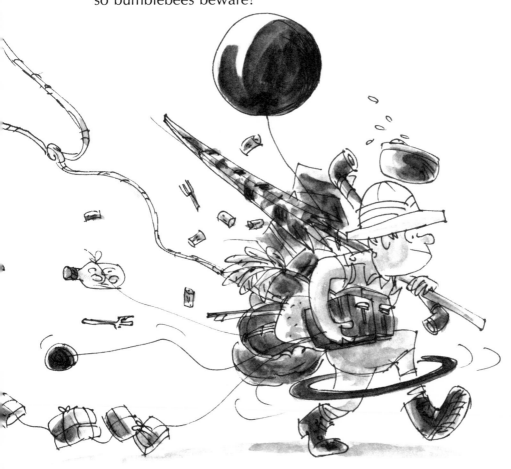

I Am Digging a Hole in the Ceiling

I am digging a hole in the ceiling
in order to gaze at the sky,
I began at the end of September,
I intend to be done by July.

I suppose I might look out the windows,
but they aren't sufficiently clean,
and it's far too much trouble to wash them,
for I haven't the proper machine.

I could leave by the door if I chose to,
I am sure I'd succeed if I tried,
but the handle's been stuck since November,
and the weather is nasty outside.

So I'm digging a hole in the ceiling
to study the sun and the moon,
I suspect it will take until summer,
for I'm using a very small spoon.

The Spider

The spider, sly and talented,
weaves silver webs of silken thread,
then waits for unobservant flies
. . . to whom she'll not apologize!

Bats

Bats have shiny leather wings,
bats do many clever things,
bats doze upside-down by day,
bats come out at night to play.

Bats cavort in soaring cliques,
sounding ultrasonic shrieks,
acrobatic in the sky,
bats catch every bug they spy.

Captain Conniption

I'm Captain Conniption,
the scourge of the sea,
no pirate alive
is as fearsome as me,
I'm ten times as tough
as the skin of a whale,
the sharks cringe in terror
wherever I sail.

I'm Captain Conniption,
the bane of the fleet,
I don't wash my face,
and I don't wash my feet,
I wear a black hat
and I fly a black flag,
I'm bad as can be,
though I don't like to brag.

When I'm on the deck
with my cutlass in hand,
the saltiest sailors
start sailing for land,
they know I'm the nastiest
nautical knave,
and bold as a brigand
is bound to behave.

I'm Captain Conniption,
and up to no good,
you'll soon walk the plank
if I think that you should,
I'd show you right now
how I vanquish a foe,
but I hear my mother,
so I have to go.

My Younger Brother's Appetite

My younger brother's appetite
is finicky, and very slight,
he's almost guaranteed to hate
whatever's placed upon his plate.
"I will not eat these greens!" he groans,
"This chicken has too many bones,
the cantaloupe is far too sweet,
there's too much gravy on the meat."

He whines, "The salad tastes like soap,
the macaroni's more like rope,
I cannot stand these soggy peas,
and I won't touch this awful cheese!"
My younger brother doesn't eat
enough to fill a parakeet.
However did he get to be
the size and shape of two of me?

I'm Sorry!

I'm sorry I squashed a banana in bed,
I'm sorry I bandaged a whole loaf of bread,
I'm sorry I pasted the prunes to your pants,
I'm sorry I brought home the ants.

I'm sorry for letting the dog eat the broom,
I'm sorry for freeing a frog in your room,
I'm sorry I wrote on the wall with sardines,
I'm sorry I sat on the beans.

I'm sorry for putting the peas in my hair,
I'm sorry for leaving the eggs on your chair,
I'm sorry for tying a can to the cat,
I'm sorry for being a brat!

We Moved About a Week Ago

We moved about a week ago,
it's nice here, I suppose,
the trouble is, I miss my friends,
like Beth, who bopped my nose,
and Jess, who liked to wrestle
and dump me in the dirt,
and Liz, who found a garter snake
and put it down my shirt.

I miss my friend Fernando,
he sometimes pulled my hair,
I miss his sister Sarah,
she shaved my teddy bear,
I miss the Trumble triplets
who dyed my sneakers blue,
and Gus, who broke my glider,
I guess I miss him too.

I really miss Melissa
who chased me up a tree,
I even miss "Gorilla" Brown
who used to sit on me,
the more I think about them,
the more it makes me sad,
I hope I make some friends here
as great as those I had.

Four Vain and Ancient Tortoises

Four vain and ancient tortoises
upon a balmy shore
were aimlessly debating
who was slowest of the four.
"I'm slowest here!" said tortoise one,
  said tortoise two, "I crawl!"
"I'm sure it's me!" said tortoise three,
  said four, "I'm worst of all!"

"We'll hold a race!" said tortoise one,
  said tortoise two, "Agreed!"
  said three and four, "We'll thus compare
  our utter lack of speed!"
"I'll lose, of course!" said tortoise one,
  said two, "I'll not prevail!"
  said three, "I'll wind up far behind!"
  said tortoise four, "I'll fail!"

Four vain and ancient tortoises
began their foolish race,
and since they were all tortoises,
they set a sluggish pace.
"I'm trailing now!" said tortoise one,
said tortoise two, "I'm last!"
"I disagree!" said tortoise three,
said four, "You're all too fast!"

Then neck and neck and neck and neck,
the finish line was crossed,
and none of them had won the race,
and none of them had lost.
"You've bested me!" said tortoise one,
said two, "My loss is sweet!"
said three, "I've shown I'm last alone!"
said four, "I've met defeat!"

And so they go on boasting
of how slowly they had run,
each futilely insisting
that the other three had won.
They argue indecisively,
no wiser than before,
four vain and ancient tortoises
upon a balmy shore.

A Goat Wandered into a Junkyard

A goat wandered into a junkyard
in search of an afternoon meal,
he started with remnants of rubber
and several fragments of steel.
He nibbled a couple of axles,
he gobbled up gauges and gears,
he gnawed on a tangle of wires
and colorful plastic veneers.

He polished off various bearings,
he munched on a mountain of brass,
he bolted a heap of upholstery
and numerous panels of glass.
He put away pistons and pedals,
then followed a fender or two
with most of a standard transmission,
and they aren't easy to chew.

He ate an assortment of sprockets,
he swallowed some springs by the coil,
then washed down his lunch with a gallon
of forty-weight premium oil.
As soon as that goat had digested
his odd but industrious meal,
he coughed and he coughed and he coughed
    and he coughed
and he coughed up an automobile.

The Disputatious Deeble

I'm the Disputatious Deeble,
who is bound to disagree
with anything at any time
you ever say to me.
"It's freezing!" you may shiver,
I'll reply, "It's far too hot!"
and if you claim, "It's raining!"
I'll rebuff you, "No! It's not!"

I'm the Disputatious Deeble,
contradictory all the time,
if you remark, "A lemon!"
I'll annunciate, "A lime!"
"Sweet butter!" you may comment,
I'll correct you, "Salty cheese!"
and if you call out, "Carrots!"
I will persevere with "Peas!"

I'm the Disputatious Deeble,
disharmonious and cross,
if you say, "Lovely gravy!"
I'll insist, "An awful sauce!"
Should you proclaim, "It's sunny!"
I'll retort, "A cloudy night!"
and I am never never wrong,
and you are never right.

I Wish My Father Wouldn't Try to Fix Things Anymore

My father's listed everything
he's planning to repair,
I hope he won't attempt it,
for the talent isn't there,
he tinkered with the toaster
when the toaster wouldn't pop,
now we keep it disconnected,
but we cannot make it stop.

He fiddled with the blender,
and he took a clock apart,
the clock is running backward,
and the blender will not start,
every windowpane he's puttied
now admits the slightest breeze,
and he's half destroyed the furnace,
if we're lucky, we won't freeze.

The TV set was working,
yet he thought he'd poke around,
now the picture's out of focus,
and there isn't any sound,
there's a faucet in the basement
that had dripped one drop all year,
since he fixed it, we can't find it
without wearing scuba gear.

I wish my father wouldn't try
to fix things anymore,
for everything he's mended
is more broken than before,
if my father finally fixes
every item on his list,
we'll be living in the garden,
for our house will not exist.

Benita Beane

Benita Beane, the trumpet queen,
makes audiences cheer,
she does not play the normal way,
she only plays by ear.

The Fuddies

The Fuddies fly above the dale,
and as they bumble by,
they leave a long and muddy trail
of footprints in the sky.

There's a Worm in My Apple

There's a worm in my apple,
a bug in my pear,
a beetle has managed
to get in my hair,
I swatted the gnat
that was nipping my ear,
and a hornet is buzzing
uncomfortably near.

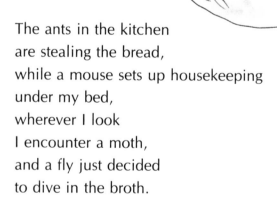

The ants in the kitchen
are stealing the bread,
while a mouse sets up housekeeping
under my bed,
wherever I look
I encounter a moth,
and a fly just decided
to dive in the broth.

There's a spider outside
that would like to move in,
a pair of mosquitoes
are riddling my chin,
the rat in the attic's
determined to stay,
I'm facing a fairly
pestiferous day.

Try Never to Tickle the Twickles

Try never to tickle the Twickles,
the Twickles, when tickled, may smile,
"We do not like smiling!" they snivel,
"It's vulgar! It's vapid! It's vile!"
If ever you tickle the Twickles,
the Twickles are likely to grin,
"Unthinkable!" whimper the Twickles,
"It ruins the shape of the chin!"

I repeat, never tickle the Twickles,
the Twickles may laugh if you do,
"It goes against nature!" they grumble,
"It's clearly considered taboo!"
Still worse, if you tickle the Twickles,
the Twickles are apt to guffaw,
"Guffawing's disgraceful!" they clamor,
"We recently made it a law!"

The Twickles you tickle will chuckle,
the Twickles you tickle will roar,
"Deplorable!" blubber the Twickles,
"It's not what we Twickles are for!
Untickled, we Twickles are grateful,
we Twickles untickled are glad,
ignore our morose dispositions,
we're happiest when we are sad!"

Warteena Weere Just Bit My Ear

Warteena Weere just bit my ear,
she mopped my face with dirt,
she popped a glop of bubblegum
and dropped it down my shirt.

She plopped her ice cream in my hair,
she bopped me with her shoe,
I think Warteena likes me—
I think I like her too!

Fuzzy, You Are Underfoot!

Fuzzy, you are underfoot!
You're never still, you won't stay put,
you twirl and try to catch your tail,
and never notice that you fail.
You clamber up and down the stairs,
depositing unsightly hairs,
and when it's time to go outside,
you scamper off and try to hide.

Fuzzy, though you understand,
you never follow my command,
I tell you "Sit!" I tell you "Stay!"
You lick my face and run away.
I buy you bones, and yet you choose
to gnaw the chair, to chew my shoes,
I would not mind a dog like that,
but you're peculiar for a cat.

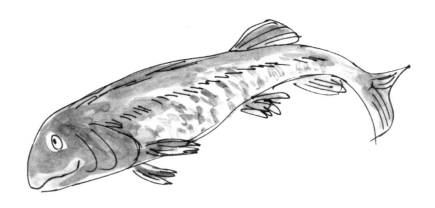

I Am Sitting Here and Fishing

I am sitting here and fishing
with my trusty rod and reel,
though I'd like to catch a snapper,
I would not refuse an eel,
and a pike would be delightful,
and a cod would be okay,
and a bass would be fantastic,
and a dace would make my day.

I am hoping for a haddock,
I am eager for a bream,
and a perch would be perfection,
and a pompano supreme,
I'd be grateful for a grunion,
I would find a flounder fine,
I'd be tickled with a pickerel
or a mackerel on my line.

But I've yet to get a nibble
at this little fishing hole,
I've not seen a single salmon
or a solitary sole,
not a miniature minnow,
not the sorriest sardine . . .
when you're fishing in the desert,
fish are few and far between.

My Woolen Sweater Itches Me

My woolen sweater itches me,
I scratch until I squeal.
Of course, I'm free to take it off . . .
just think how sheep must feel!

I'm Much Too Tired to Play Tonight

I'm much too tired to play tonight,
I'm much too tired to talk,
I'm much too tired to pet the dog
or take him for a walk,
I'm much too tired to bounce a ball,
I'm much too tired to sing,
I'm much too tired to try to think
about a single thing.

I'm much too tired to laugh tonight,
I'm much too tired to smile,
I'm much too tired to watch TV
or read a little while,
I'm much too tired to drink my milk
or even nod my head,
but I'm not nearly tired enough
to have to go to bed.

My Snake

My snake, a long and limber pet,

is practicing the alphabet,

he demonstrates immense finesse

in shaping a curvaceous S.

He follows his initial show

by closing up into an O,

then fabricates an F and G

with enviable artistry.

My snake, with neither pad nor pen,

delineates a splendid N,

an agile H, a supple L,

an X with little parallel,

a shapely J, a graceful A,

a seamless C, a clever K,

then pausing for a breath or two,

he turns himself into a U.

116

My snake, with every skillful twist,

appends a letter to his list,

he makes an *E*, he forms an *M*,

a *Y* and *V* come after them,

he diagrams a dextrous *D*,

a subtle *T*, a nimble *Z*,

a convoluted curly *O*,

a virtuoso *W*.

My snake, performing like a star,

portrays a *P*, enacts an *R*,

contorts into a brilliant *B*

with stylish sinuosity.

And yet, though he may stretch and shake,

one single point eludes my snake,

despite his most ingenious try,

he simply cannot dot his *I*.

My Brother Is a Quarterback

My brother is a quarterback,
I rarely catch a pass,
and he can run a marathon,
I soon run out of gas,
he pitches for his baseball team,
I pop up on his curve,
and he's an ace at tennis,
I can't return his serve.

My brother dunks the basketball,
I dribble like a mule,
he swims like a torpedo,
I flounder in the pool,
he's accurate at archery,
I hardly ever score,
he boxes and he wrestles,
I wind up on the floor.

My brother catches lots of fish,
I haven't any luck,
he's captain of his hockey team,
I can't control the puck,
his bowling's unbelievable,
I bowl like a buffoon,
he says someday I'll start to win . . .
I hope someday is soon.

I Want a Pet Porcupine, Mother

"I want a pet porcupine, Mother!"
I said to her early today,
she chuckled, "It's out of the question,
I wish you would go out and play."

"Then, Mother, I want a gorilla,
or else I would like a giraffe!"
she answered without hesitation,
"Ridiculous! Don't make me laugh!"

"Then, Mother, I want an iguana,
 a burro, a boar, or a bear!"
 she seemed to start growing impatient,
 she shouted, "Get out of my hair!"

"Then, Mother, I want a pet lion,
 I'm certain a lion would do,
 I'd take him for walks every Sunday
 to visit his friends in the zoo!"

"You can't have a lion!" she told me,
"Be glad with the pet that you've got!"
 I guess we're just keeping the rhino,
 she's always liked Rhona a lot.

Mold, Mold

Mold, mold,
marvelous mold,
alluring to look at,
enthralling to hold,
you are so delightful
I can't help but smile
when I nuzzle a smidgen
of mold for awhile.

Slime, slime,
savory slime,
you're luscious and succulent
any old time,
there's hardly a thing
that is nearly as grand
as a dollop of slime
in the palm of my hand.

Some think you are miserable
manners of muck,
they can't stand to see you,
you make them say, "Yuck!"
But I think you're fetching,
beguiling and fine,
mold, you are glorious,
slime, you're divine.

My Family's Sleeping Late Today

My family's sleeping late today,
but I am wide awake,
and making all the racket
it is possible to make.
I'm rapping on a window pane,
I'm hammering a nail,
I'm playing tackle with the cat,
and yanking on her tail.

I'm racing madly through the house,
I'm slamming every door,
I'm imitating jungle sounds,
I trumpet and I roar.
I think I'll play my tambourine
and pop a big balloon,
they'll never sleep through all of that,
they're sure to get up soon.

I Did Not Eat Your Ice Cream

I did not eat your ice cream,
I did not swipe your socks,
I did not stuff your lunch box
with rubber bands and rocks.

I did not hide your sweater,
I did not dent your bike,
it must have been my sister,
we look a lot alike.

Sir Bottomwide

Sir Bottomwide, a stalwart knight,
was absolutely blue,
he sniveled inconsolably,
he sobbed the whole day through,
he blubbered as he clanked about,
he cried astride his horse,
the teardrops flooded from his eyes
with unabated force.

They fell upon his pillow
while he slumbered in his bed,
they leaked into his regal ears,
they drenched his noble head.
Sir Bottomwide had cause to be
a most unhappy knight,
his cast-iron armored underwear
was half a size too tight.

The Moodles Have No Middles

The Moodles have no middles,
though they're otherwise complete,
their faces are bass fiddles,
which they play upon the street.
It's apparent, if you've seen them
in their bands of tens and twelves,
that there's nothing in-between them
to connect them to themselves.

The Moodles love to chatter,
and the Moodles love to sport,
despite a lack of matter
to provide them with support.
It's a mystifying riddle
that's impossible to guess,
how those Moodles with no middles
can survive with such success.

The Barber of Shrubbery Hollow

I'm the barber of Shrubbery Hollow,
I need neither clippers nor comb,
I never trim anyone's whiskers,
nor manicure anyone's dome.
My services aren't required,
no customers come to my shop
requesting a shave and a haircut,
not even "a bit off the top!"

I'm the barber of Shrubbery Hollow,
with practically nothing to do,
I spend the day sharpening scissors
or giving my shoes a shampoo.
I might as well go out of business
and give up this boring routine,
for why bother being a barber
where everyone's bald as a bean?

Picklepuss Pearl

I'm Picklepuss Pearl, and I'm not very nice,
I'm not made of sugar, I'm not made of spice,
my attitude's awful, my temper is vile,
I have no idea what it feels like to smile.

I'm Picklepuss Pearl, and I'm nasty and sour,
my wretched expression can wither a flower,
it takes but a blink of my miserable eye
for laughing hyenas to break down and cry.

If I fix your face with my permanent frown,
your stomach is liable to turn upside-down,
my stare is so cold it turns water to ice,
I'm Picklepuss Pearl, and I'm not very nice.

My Brother Is as Generous as Anyone Could Be

My brother is as generous
as anyone could be,
for everything he's ever had
he's always shared with me.
He has loaned me his binoculars,
his new computer games,
and his wind-up walking dragon
that breathes artificial flames.

I've been grateful for his robots,
for his giant teddy bear,
but not for certain other things
I'd hoped he'd never share—
Though I'm glad he's shared his rockets
and his magic jumping rocks,
I wish my brother hadn't shared
his case of chicken pox.

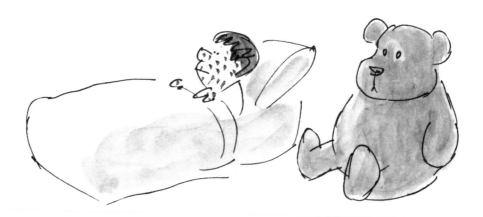

I Lost My Invisible Puppy

I lost my invisible puppy
when we were out walking today,
she disappeared into the bushes
and totally faded away.

My puppy is not too apparent,
my puppy is paler than pale,
she tends not to draw much attention,
she wags an invisible tail.

She wears an invisible collar,
her leash is invisible too,
I fear that she's vanished forever,
she's totally hidden from view.

I'll miss her obscure little antics,
her odd indiscernible tricks,
she chased inconspicuous crickets,
she fetched undetectable sticks.

My poor imperceptible puppy
is probably still in the park,
perhaps if I pay close attention,
I'll hear her inaudible bark.

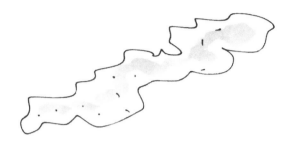

The Smoking Yokadokas

We're the Smoking Yokadokas,
we sincerely need to smoke,
and we do not mind the slightest
that our smoking makes you choke,
our malodorous miasma
will assail you when we're near,
it will irritate your nostrils
and compel your eyes to tear.

We're the Smoking Yokadokas,
we're not nice to have around,
you can often hear us coughing,
it's a coarse and raucous sound,
all our teeth are brown and yellow,
and our breath is always stale,
we're especially offensive
at the moment we exhale.

Our appearance is unsightly,
we have ashes on our clothes,
our aroma is appalling,
you may have to hold your nose,
but don't waste your time complaining
we contaminate the air,
we're the Smoking Yokadokas,
and we simply do not care.

Mosquitoes, Mosquitoes!

Mosquitoes, mosquitoes,
stop torturing me,
why can't you behave
more considerately,
you've bitten me practically
down to the bone,
mosquitoes, mosquitoes,
please leave me alone!

Mosquitoes, mosquitoes,
you're hard to ignore,
I itch and I scratch,
I can't stand anymore,
you've bitten my bottom,
you've bitten my top,
mosquitoes, mosquitoes,
I'm begging you, stop!

Mosquitoes, mosquitoes,
I honestly feel
it's time that you went
somewhere else for a meal,
you've bitten me places
I can't even see,
mosquitoes, mosquitoes,
stop torturing me!

I Saw a Brontosaurus

I saw a brontosaurus
saunter through my neighborhood,
this struck me as peculiar,
as I'd heard they'd gone for good,
its proportions were imposing,
it was long and tall and wide,
I ran home to fetch a ladder,
then ascended for a ride.

It was hard to sit astride it,
for its hide was rather rough
and I had to ride it bareback,
there's no saddle big enough,
it turned into the sunset
and we started heading west,
my parents seemed uneasy,
but the neighbors looked impressed.

138

We squeezed between the buildings
as we thundered out of town,
the beast became rambunctious,
and it bounded up and down,
it ignored my agitation
and my frequent shouts of "Whoa!"
and I almost bounced to pieces
as we crossed a wide plateau.

That brontosaurus tossed me
in the middle of a plain,
I landed in a wheat field,
where I fell against the grain,
though I treasure my adventure,
I won't do it anymore,
for that bucking brontosaurus
made my bottom bronto**sore!**

Rhododendra Rosenbloom

Rhododendra Rosenbloom
loves the smell of fine perfume,
she went to the corner store,
there she bought perfumes galore—

BUTTERCUP BANANA PEEL

CATERPILLAR CAMOMILE

ROSE REPUGNANT RAT REGRET

VINYL VIPER VIOLET

GREEN FARINA WILLOW THRILL

DROMEDARY DAFFODIL

FRANGIAPANI FINGERNAIL

GLADIOLA GARBAGE PAIL

SLOPPY GUPPY POPPY PINE

TULIP TURTLE TURPENTINE

Rhododendra Rosenbloom
bought ten kinds of fine perfume,
she could not have purchased more—
it was just a ten scent store!

140

I'm Certain I Sing Like an Angel

I'm certain I sing like an angel,
I have a mellifluous voice,
the moment I open my musical mouth,
the multitudes ought to rejoice.

I croon with melodic precision
in tones undeniably sweet,
I wonder why people throw water at me
whenever I sing in the street.

Why Do I Water My Flowers?

Why do I water my flowers?
Why do I turn on the hose
to bathe my beloved begonias
and spray every beautiful rose?
Why do I tend to my tulips
and cover them lightly with dew?
Why do I sprinkle my lilacs?
I haven't come up with a clue.

Why do I drench my azaleas,
carnations, and sweet columbine?
Why do I dampen the blossoms
that grace my wisteria vine?
It's foolish to water my flowers,
I really don't know why I try—
They're all manufactured of plastic,
and manage just fine when they're dry.

142

Super Samson Simpson

I am Super Samson Simpson,
I'm superlatively strong,
I like to carry elephants,
I do it all day long,
I pick up half a dozen
and hoist them in the air,
it's really somewhat simple,
for I have strength to spare.

My muscles are enormous,
they bulge from top to toe,
and when I carry elephants,
they ripple to and fro,
but I am not the strongest
in the Simpson family,
for when I carry elephants,
my grandma carries me.

143

As Soon as Penny Goes to Bed

As soon as Penny goes to bed,
she screeches and she cries,
she tosses on her pillow
and she cannot shut her eyes.

She whimpers and she snivels
and she blubbers and she wails. . . .
poor Penny should not try to sleep
upon a bed of nails.

The Wumpaloons, Which Never Were

The Wumpaloons, which never were,
had silver scales and purple fur,
their wings were alabaster white,
their manes as black as anthracite,
their legs were pink and indigo,
with toes of bright pistachio,
their noses were a bottle green,
their antlers tan and tangerine.

The Wumpaloons had crimson lips,
their tails were teal, with flaxen tips,
their lilac eyes were flecked with dots
as gold as summer apricots,
their necks were lemon, striped with blue,
their ears were of a ruby hue.
How nice to think they might occur,
the Wumpaloons, which never were.

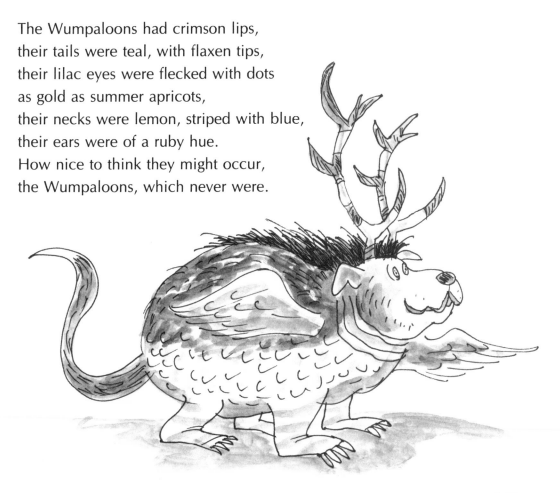

My Fish Can Ride a Bicycle

My fish can ride a bicycle,
my fish can climb a tree,
my fish enjoys a glass of milk,
my fish takes naps with me.

My fish can play the clarinet,
my fish can bounce a ball,
my fish is not like other fish,
my fish can't swim at all.

My Sister Ate an Orange

My sister ate an orange,
I'm astonished that she did,
she swallowed it completely,
she's a disconcerting kid.

My sister ate an orange,
first she chewed it for awhile,
then digested it entirely
with a silly sort of smile.

My sister ate an orange,
it's a novel thing to do,
then she also ate a yellow
and a purple and a blue.

An Elephant Is Hard to Hide

An elephant is hard to hide,
it's rather tall, it's fairly wide,
it occupies a lot of space,
you just can't put it anyplace.
It's quite an unrewarding chore
to try and cram it in a drawer,
a closet's somewhat better, but
you're apt to find the door won't shut.

An elephant beneath your bed
will manifest both tail and head,
and in the tub, there's little doubt
that it will soon be singled out.
An elephant won't simply sit,
it tends to move about a bit,
this trait, when coupled with its size
makes it a nightmare to disguise.

An elephant, if kept around
is almost certain to be found,
your parents may suspect one's near
when peanuts start to disappear.
An elephant is hard to hide,
I know it's so, because I've tried,
my family should detect mine soon . . .
I brought it home this afternoon.

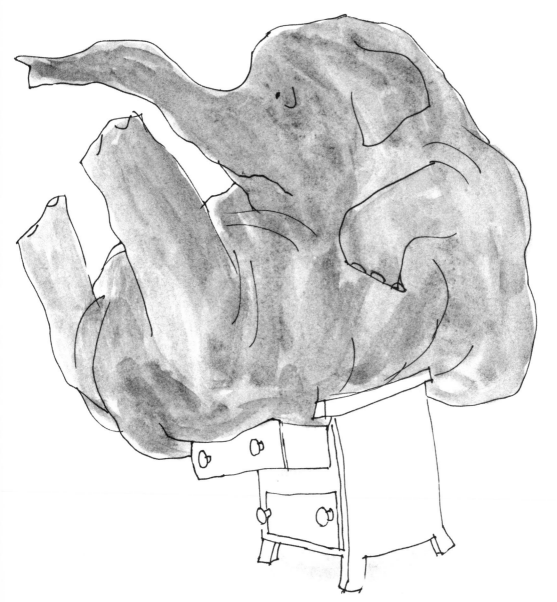

Mother Goblin's Lullaby

Go to sleep, my baby goblin,
hushaby, my dear of dears,
if you disobey your mother,
she will twist your pointed ears.

Little goblin, stop complaining,
time for all your eyes to close,
if you make your mother angry,
she will bite your tiny nose.

Slumber sweetly till tomorrow,
do not worry, Mother's near,
dream of demons weirdly screaming,
hushaby, my goblin dear.

My Brother's Bug

My brother's bug was green and plump,
it did not run, it could not jump,
it had no fur for it to shed,
it slept all night beneath his bed.

My brother's bug had dainty feet,
it did not need a lot to eat,
it did not need a lot to drink,
it did not scream, it did not stink.

It always tried to be polite,
it did not scratch, it did not bite,
the only time it soiled the rug
was when I squashed my brother's bug.

151

We're Fearless Flying Hot Dogs

We're fearless flying hot dogs,
the famous "Unflappable Five,"
we're mustered in formation
to climb, to dip, to dive,
we spread our wings with relish,
then reach for altitude,
we're aerobatic wieners,
the fastest flying food.

We're fearless flying hot dogs,
we race with flair and style,
then catch up with each other
and soar in single file,
you never saw such daring,
such power and control,
as when we swoop and spiral,
then slide into a roll.

The throngs applaud our antics,
they cheer us long and loud,
there's never a chilly reception,
there's never a sour crowd,
and if we may speak frankly,
we are a thrilling sight,
we're fearless flying hot dogs,
the delicate essence of flight.

Index to Titles

Addle-pated Paddlepuss, The, 60
As Soon As Fred Gets Out of Bed, 14
As Soon as Penny Goes to Bed, 144
Auk in Flight, An, 48

Barber of Shrubbery Hollow, The, 128
Bats, 89
Belinda Blue, 16
Benita Beane, 104

Captain Conniption, 90

Denson Dumm, 22
Disputatious Deeble, The, 100
Do Not Disturb the Woolly Wurbbe, 40
Don't Yell at Me!, 75

Early Worm Got Out of Bed, An, 8
Elephant Is Hard to Hide, An, 148

Fenton Phlantz, 49
Four Vain and Ancient Tortoises, 96
Fuddies, The, 105
Fuzzy, You Are Underfoot!, 111

Goat Wandered into a Junkyard, A, 98
Grasshopper Gumbo, 52

Happy Birthday, Mother Dearest, 10
Hello! How Are You? I Am Fine!, 36

I Am a Ghost Who's Lost His Boo, 42
I Am Digging a Hole in the Ceiling, 86
I Am Growing a Glorious Garden, 12
I Am Sitting Here and Fishing, 112
I Am Tired of Being Little, 24
I Am Wunk, 20
I Did Not Eat Your Ice Cream, 125
I Know All the Sounds that the Animals Make, 9
I Lost My Invisible Puppy, 132
I'm Certain I Sing Like an Angel, 141

I Met a Rat of Culture, 38
I'm Much Too Tired to Play Tonight, 115
I'm Off to Catch a Bumblebee, 84
I'm Sorry!, 93
I Saw a Brontosaurus, 138
I Should Have Stayed in Bed Today, 28
I Want a Pet Porcupine, Mother, 120
I Wave Good-bye When Butter Flies, 80
I Wish My Father Wouldn't Try to Fix Things Anymore, 102

Katy Ate a Baked Potato, 59
Kevin the King of the Jungle, 30

Last Night I Dreamed of Chickens, 44
Life's Not Been the Same in My Family, 37
Little Bird Outside My Window, 32

Mold, Mold, 122
Moodles Have No Middles, The, 127
Mosquitoes, Mosquitoes!, 136
Mother Goblin's Lullaby, 150
My Brother Built a Robot, 46
My Brother Is a Quarterback, 118
My Brother Is as Generous as Anyone Could Be, 130
My Brother's Bug, 151
My Family's Sleeping Late Today, 124
My Fish Can Ride a Bicycle, 146
My Frog Is a Frog, 82
My Mother Made a Meat Loaf, 66
My Neighbor's Dog Is Purple, 41
My Sister Ate an Orange, 147
My Snake, 116
My Uncle Looked Me in the Eye, 50
My Woolen Sweater Itches Me, 114
My Younger Brother's Appetite, 92

Nigel Gline, 76

Picklepuss Pearl, 129

Rains in Little Dribbles, The, 53
Remarkable Adventure, A, 56
Rhododendra Rosenbloom, 140

Sir Bottomwide, 126
Slow Sloth's Slow Song, 65
Smoking Yokadokas, The, 134
Something Big Has Been Here, 7
Spider, The, 88
Squirrels, 58
Super Samson Simpson, 143

There's a Worm in My Apple, 106
There's No One as Slow as Slomona, 74
They Never Send Sam to the Store Anymore, 78
They Tell Me I'm Peculiar, 27
Today I'm Going Yesterday, 72
Today I Shall Powder My Elephant's Ears, 54
Try Never to Tickle the Twickles, 108
Turkey Shot out of the Oven, The, 18
Twaddletalk Tuck, 64

Unhappy South Pole Penguin, 33

Warteena Weere Just Bit My Ear, 110
Watson Watts, 34
We Moved About a Week Ago, 94
We're Fearless Flying Hot Dogs, 152
We're Four Ferocious Tigers, 11
We're Know-nothing Neebies, 68
Who Pulled the Plug in My Ant Farm?, 70
Why Do I Water My Flowers?, 142
Wilhelmina Wafflewitz, 83
Wumpaloons, Which Never Were, The, 145

You're Eating Like a Pig Again!, 23
You're Nasty and You're Loud, 26

Zoo Was in an Uproar, The, 62

156

Index to First Lines

A goat wandered into a junkyard, 98
An auk in flight, 48
An early worm got out of bed, 8
An elephant is hard to hide, 148
As soon as Fred gets out of bed, 14
As soon as Penny goes to bed, 144

Bats have shiny leather wings, 89
Belinda Blue was furious, 16
Benita Beane, the trumpet queen, 104

Denson Dumm, with pomp and flair, 22
Do not disturb the woolly Wurbbe, 40
Don't yell at me!, 75

Fenton Phlantz is fairly weird, 49
Four vain and ancient tortoises, 96
Fuzzy, you are underfoot!, 111

Go to sleep, my baby goblin, 150
Grasshopper Gumbo, 52

Happy birthday, Mother dearest, 10
Hello! How are you? I am fine!, 36

I am a ghost who's lost his boo, 42
I.......am.......a.......sloth......., 65
I am digging a hole in the ceiling, 86
I am growing a glorious garden, 12
I am sitting here and fishing, 112
I am Super Samson Simpson, 143
I am tired of being little, 24
I am Wunk, a wacky wizard, 20
I did not eat your ice cream, 125
I know all the sounds that the animals make, 9
I lost my invisible puppy, 132
I'm Captain Conniption, 90
I'm certain I sing like an angel, 141
I met a rat of culture, 38
I'm Kevin the king of the jungle, 30

I'm much too tired to play tonight, 115
I'm off to catch a bumblebee, 84
I'm Picklepuss Pearl, and I'm not very nice, 129
I'm sorry I squashed a banana in bed, 93
I'm the barber of Shrubbery Hollow, 128
I'm the Disputatious Deeble, 100
I'm Twaddletalk Tuck and I talk and I talk, 64
I'm Wilhelmina Wafflewitz, 83
I saw a brontosaurus, 138
I should have stayed in bed today, 28
"I want a pet porcupine, Mother!," 120
I was at my bedroom table, 56
I wave good-bye when butter flies, 80

Katy ate a baked potato, strolling through the mews, 59

Last night I dreamed of chickens, 44
Life's not been the same in my family, 37
Little bird outside my window, 32

Mold, mold, 122
Mosquitoes, mosquitoes, 136
My brother built a robot, 46
My brother is a quarterback, 118
My brother is as generous, 130
My brother's bug was green and plump, 151
My family's sleeping late today, 124
My father's listed everything, 102
My fish can ride a bicycle, 146
My frog is a frog that is hopelessly hoarse, 82
My mother made a meat loaf, 66
My neighbor's dog is purple, 41
My sister ate an orange, 147
My snake, a long and limber pet, 116
My uncle looked me in the eye, 50
My woolen sweater itches me, 114
My younger brother's appetite, 92

Rhododendra Rosenbloom, 140

Sir Bottomwide, a stalwart knight, 126
Something big has been here, 7
Squirrels, often found in parks, 58

The Addle-pated Paddlepuss, 60
The day they sent Sam to the grocery store, 78
The Fuddies fly above the dale, 105
The Moodles have no middles, 127
The rains in Little Dribbles, 53
The spider, sly and talented, 88
The turkey shot out of the oven, 18
The Wumpaloons, which never were, 145
The zoo was in an uproar, 62
There's a worm in my apple, 106
There's no one as slow as Slomona, 74
They tell me I'm peculiar, 27
Today I'm going yesterday, 72
Today I shall powder my elephant's ears, 54
Try never to tickle the Twickles, 108

Unhappy South Pole penguin, 33

Warteena Weere just bit my ear, 110
Watson Watts, atop his head, 34
We moved about a week ago, 94
We're fearless flying hot dogs, 152
We're four ferocious tigers, 11
We're Know-nothing Neebies, 68
We're the Smoking Yokadokas, 134
When Nigel Gline sat down to dine, 76
Who pulled the plug in my ant farm?, 70
Why do I water my flowers?, 142

"You're eating like a pig again!," 23
You're nasty and you're loud, 26

OTHER BOOKS BY JACK PRELUTSKY

The Baby Uggs Are Hatching
Beneath a Blue Umbrella
The Headless Horseman Rides Tonight
It's Christmas
It's Halloween
It's Snowing! It's Snowing!
It's Thanksgiving
It's Valentine's Day
The Mean Old Mean Hyena
My Parents Think I'm Sleeping
The New Kid on the Block
Nightmares
The Queen of Eene
Rainy Rainy Saturday
Ride a Purple Pelican
Rolling Harvey Down the Hill
The Sheriff of Rottenshot
The Snopp on the Sidewalk
Tyrannosaurus Was a Beast
What I Did Last Summer
The Wild Baby by Barbro Lindgren (*translation*)
The Wild Baby Gets a Puppy by Barbro Lindgren (*translation*)
The Wild Baby Goes to Sea by Barbro Lindgren (*translation*)
Zoo Doings

OTHER BOOKS BY JACK PRELUTSKY

The Baby Uggs Are Hatching
The Headless Horseman Rides Tonight
It's Christmas
It's Halloween
It's Snowing! It's Snowing!
It's Thanksgiving
It's Valentine's Day
The Mean Old Mean Hyena
Nightmares
The Queen of Eene
Rainy Rainy Saturday
Rolling Harvey down the Hill
The Sheriff of Rottenshot
The Snopp on the Sidewalk
What I Did Last Summer
The Wild Baby by Barbro Lindgren *(translation)*
The Wild Baby Goes to Sea by Barbro Lindgren *(translation)*
Zoo Doings

The Bloders are exploding, 37
The carpenter rages, the carpenter rants, 40
The Cherries' garden gala, 80
The cuckoo in our cuckoo clock, 19
The Diatonic Dittymunch, 132
The duo met to duel at dawn, 92
The flimsy Fleek is mild and meek, 106
The greatest ace of video space, 150
The neighbors are not fond of me, 33
The poorest juggler ever seen, 10
The shrewdest salesman anywhere, 144
The Underwater Wibbles, 16
There is a thing, 119
There were rumbles of strange jubilation, 152
There's a new kid on the block, 7
There's an irritating creature, 84
There's no one as immaculate, 44
There's no one mean as mean Maxine, 66
Throckmorton Thratte has charm and class, 94
Today is a day to crow about, 73
Today is very boring, 96

Uncanny Colleen (unaccountably green), 95

We are Gloppers, gloopy Gloppers, 58
We each wore half a horse, 67
We heard Wally wail through the whole neighborhood, 42
We're FORTY PERFORMING BANANAS, 147
What nerve you've got, Minerva Mott!, 43
When Dracula went to the blood bank, 114
When the summer sun is blazing, 99
When Tillie ate the chili, 88
When young, the Slyne, from noon to nine, 115
"With chopsticks did I sip my soup," 118

You may quarrel with centipedes, quibble with seals, 89
You need to have an iron rear, 15
Yubbazubbies, you are yummy, 68

159

The New Kid on the Block

The New Kid

on the Block

poems by JACK PRELUTSKY
drawings by JAMES STEVENSON

 Greenwillow Books, New York

ISBN 978-0-06-171372-9

 Greenwillow Books

For Susan Hirschman
—20 years—

The New Kid on the Block

There's a new kid on the block,
and boy, that kid is tough,
that new kid punches hard,
that new kid plays real rough,
that new kid's big and strong,
with muscles everywhere,
that new kid tweaked my arm,
that new kid pulled my hair.

That new kid likes to fight,
and picks on all the guys,
that new kid scares me some,
(that new kid's twice my size),
that new kid stomped my toes,
that new kid swiped my ball,
that new kid's really bad,
I don't care for her at all.

Jellyfish Stew

Jellyfish stew,
I'm loony for you,
I dearly adore you,
oh, truly I do,
you're creepy to see,
revolting to chew,
you slide down inside
with a hullabaloo.

You're soggy, you're smelly,
you taste like shampoo,
you bog down my belly
with oodles of goo,
yet I would glue noodles
and prunes to my shoe,
for one oozy spoonful
of jellyfish stew.

Nine Mice

Nine mice on tiny tricycles
went riding on the ice,
they rode in spite of warning signs,
they rode despite advice.

The signs were right, the ice was thin,
in half a trice, the mice fell in,
and from their chins down to their toes,
those mice entirely froze.

Nine mindless mice, who paid the price,
are thawing slowly by the ice,
still sitting on their tricycles
. . . nine white and shiny *micicles!*

Clara Cleech

The poorest juggler ever seen
was clumsy Clara Cleech,
who juggled a bean, a nectarine,
a pumpkin, and a peach.

She juggled a stone, a slide trombone,
a celery stalk, a stick,
a seeded roll, a salad bowl,
a bagel, a boot, a brick.

With relative ease she juggled a cheese,
she juggled a lock, a lime,
yes, Clara juggled all of these
. . . *but just one at a time.*

I Wonder Why Dad Is So Thoroughly Mad

I wonder why Dad is so thoroughly mad,
I can't understand it at all,
unless it's the bee still afloat in his tea,
or his underwear, pinned to the wall.

Perhaps it's the dye on his favorite tie,
or the mousetrap that snapped in his shoe,
or the pipeful of gum that he found with his thumb,
or the toilet, sealed tightly with glue.

It can't be the bread crumbled up in his bed,
or the slugs someone left in the hall,
I wonder why Dad is so thoroughly mad,
I can't understand it at all.

Drumpp the Grump

I'm Drumpp, the grump of the garbage dump,
I'm a contradictory cuss,
I'm grubby and gruff, and just as rough
as an old rhinoceros.

I never wash, and like to squash
my fingers into worms,
I'm full of fleas and smelly cheese
and fifty million germs.

I swallow food before it's chewed,
I belch an awful lot,
I smell like a goat, and wear a coat
that swarms with slime and rot.

I'm mean as a bear that's burned his hair,
I've nothing nice to say,
I don't like you . . . or *you* . . . or YOU!
You'd better go away.

I'm Drumpp, the grump of the garbage dump,
I'm hard as a battering ram,
but I want you to know before you go . . .
I LIKE THE WAY I AM!

Alligators Are Unfriendly

Alligators are unfriendly,
they are easily upset,
I suspect that I would never
care to have one for a pet.
Oh, I know they do not bellow,
and I think they do not shed,
but I'd probably be nervous
if I had one in my bed.

Alligators are not clever,
they are something of a bore,
they can't heel or catch a Frisbee,
they don't greet you at the door,
for their courtesy is lacking,
and their tempers are not sweet,
they won't even fetch your slippers
. . . though they just might eat your feet.

You Need to Have an Iron Rear

You need to have an iron rear
to sit upon a cactus,
or otherwise, at least a year
of very painful practice.

The Underwater Wibbles

The Underwater Wibbles
dine exclusively on cheese,
they keep it in containers
which they bind about their knees,
they often chew on Cheddar
which they slice into a dish,
and gorge on Gorgonzola
to the wonder of the fish.

The Underwater Wibbles
wiggle blithely through the sea,
munching merrily on Muenster,
grated Feta, bits of Brie,
passing porpoises seem puzzled,
stolid octopuses stare,
as the Wibbles nibble Gouda,
Provolone, Camembert.

The Underwater Wibbles
frolic gaily off the coast,
eating melted Mozzarella
served on soggy crusts of toast,
Wibbles gobble Appenzeller
as they execute their dives,
oh, the Underwater Wibbles
live extraordinary lives.

I Am Running in a Circle

I am running in a circle
and my feet are getting sore,
and my head is
spinning
spinning
as it's never spun before,
I am
dizzy
dizzy
dizzy.
Oh! I cannot bear much more,
I am trapped in a
revolving
. . . volving
. . . volving
. . . volving door!

<u>Cuckoo!</u>

The cuckoo in our cuckoo clock
was wedded to an octopus,
she laid a single wooden egg,
and hatched a cuckoocloctopus.

Do Oysters Sneeze?

Do oysters sneeze beneath the seas,
or wiggle to and fro,
or sulk, or smile, or dance awhile
. . . how can we ever know?

Do oysters yawn when roused at dawn,
and do they ever weep,
and can we tell, when, in its shell,
an oyster is asleep?

Mabel, Remarkable Mabel

Oh, Mabel, remarkable Mabel,
your dining demeanor is queer,
you eat with your feet on the table,
while a teaspoon sticks out of your ear.

Your mouth opens wide and then wider,
as you shovel six hamburgers in,
your elbows are dripping with cider,
there is mustard all over your chin.

In your lap lies a lump of linguine,
your toes cling to slices of bread,
your knees balance pounds of zucchini,
there's a pudding on top of your head.

Your nose is spread thickly with butter,
your shoulders hold pickles in brine.
Oh, Mabel, you may make me mutter,
but it's wonderful watching you dine.

Its Fangs Were Red

Its fangs were red with bloody gore,
its eyes were red with menace,
it battered down my bedroom door,
and burst across my bedroom floor,
and with a loud, resounding roar
said, *"ANYONE FOR TENNIS?"*

An Unassuming Owl

An unassuming owl,
having little else to do,
remarked within the darkness
a discreet and subtle "WHOOOOOOOOOOOO!"

A self-important owl,
puffed and pompous in the gloom,
responded with an overblown
and condescending
   *"WHOOOOOOOOOOOOOOOOOOOOO
   OOOOOOOOOOM!"*

I've Got an Itch

I've got an itch, a wretched itch,
no other itch could match it,
it itches in the one spot which
I cannot reach, to scratch it.

Snillies

In the middle of a lily,
if you're fortunate, you'll find
little Snillies, dim and silly,
not a one has any mind.

Snillies move in mass confusion,
hopping here and skipping there,
yet they reach no firm conclusion,
though at times they stop and stare.

Snillies fail to eat their dinner,
Snillies let their lunch slip by,
every day they're growing thinner,
yet they can't imagine why.

Euphonica Jarre

Euphonica Jarre has a voice that's bizarre,
but Euphonica warbles all day,
as windowpanes shatter and chefs spoil the batter
and mannequins moan with dismay.

Mighty ships run aground at her horrible sound,
pretty pictures fall out of their frames,
trees drop off their branches,
rocks start avalanches,
and flower beds burst into flames.

When she opens her mouth, even eagles head south,
little fish truly wish they could drown,
the buzzards all hover, as tigers take cover,
and rats pack their bags and leave town.

Milk turns into butter and butterflies mutter
and bees look for something to sting,
pigs peel off their skins, a tornado begins
when Euphonica Jarre starts to sing.

I'm Thankful

I'm thankful for my baseball bat,
I cracked it yesterday,
I'm thankful for my checker set,
I haven't learned to play,
I'm thankful for my mittens,
one is missing in the snow,
I'm thankful for my hamsters,
they escaped a month ago.

I'm thankful for my basketball,
it's sprung another leak,
I'm thankful for my parakeet,
it bit me twice last week,
I'm thankful for my bicycle,
I crashed into a tree,
I'm thankful for my roller skates,
I fell and scraped my knee.

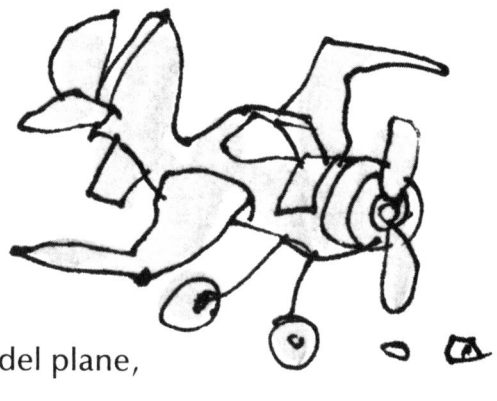

I'm thankful for my model plane,
it's short a dozen parts,
I'm thankful for my target game,
I'm sure I'll find the darts,
I'm thankful for my bathing suit,
it came off in the river,
I'm thankful for so many things,
except, of course, for LIVER!

A Wolf Is at the Laundromat

A wolf is at the Laundromat,
it's not a wary stare-wolf,
it's short and fat, it tips its hat,
unlike a scary glare-wolf.

It combs its hair, it clips its toes,
it is a fairly rare wolf,
that's only there to clean its clothes—
it is a wash–and–wear–wolf.

No, I *Won't* Turn Orange!

No, I *won't* turn orange
if I eat this orange,
so don't you give me that!
No, I *won't* turn orange
if I eat this orange,
you're talking through your hat!

No, I *won't* turn orange
if I eat this orange,
that's just a bunch of stuff!
No, I *won't* turn orange
if I eat this orange,
I'm going to call your bluff!

No, I *won't* turn orange
if I eat this orange,
so who are you trying to kid?
No, I *won't* turn orange
if I eat this orange. . . .
Well, what do you know,
I DID!

Granny Grizer

Granny Grizer, greedy miser,
is immeasurably mean,
if she sees that you are hungry,
she won't offer you a bean,
she's so absolutely selfish,
she'd deny a dog a bone,
if she owned a million mountains,
no one else would have a stone.

She would charge you for her shadow,
she would charge you for a splinter,
she would charge you for a snowflake
in the middle of the winter,
for she clings to every nickel,
every button, every crumb,
Granny Grizer, greedy miser,
is as stingy as they come.

The Neighbors Are Not Fond of Me

The neighbors are not fond of me,
I've little doubt of that,
for when I near their door, I see
they hide the WELCOME mat.

Ah! A Monster's Lot Is Merry

Ah! A monster's lot is merry
in the melancholy swamp,
here I'm free to be offensive,
free to frolic, free to romp,
what a lark it is to muddle
in the middle of the murk,
making nauseating noises,
driving birds a bit berserk.

There is nothing quite so pleasant
as a solitary trudge
through the wretched desolation
of the pestilential sludge,
how divine to wade and wallow,
and I find I never tire
of distressing little fishes
as I dive beneath the mire.

It's despicably delicious
to disport about the bogs,
making disconcerting faces,
discombobulating frogs,
I consider, as I slither
through an endless sea of slime,
that a monster's lot is merry,
so I'm merry all the time.

Louder than a Clap of Thunder!

Louder than a clap of thunder,
louder than an eagle screams,
louder than a dragon blunders,
or a dozen football teams,
louder than a four-alarmer,
or a rushing waterfall,
louder than a knight in armor
jumping from a ten-foot wall.

Louder than an earthquake rumbles,
louder than a tidal wave,
louder than an ogre grumbles
as he stumbles through his cave,
louder than stampeding cattle,
louder than a cannon roars,
louder than a giant's rattle,
that's how loud my father *SNORES!*

The Bloders Are Exploding

The Bloders are exploding,
they are bursting left and right,
like vials of nitroglycerine,
or sticks of dynamite.

They are going up like rockets,
they are popping here and there,
the sky is filled with Bloders
detonating in the air.

There's a simple explanation
for this odd catastrophe,
you are bound to go to pieces
when you dine on TNT.

Sneaky Sue

I am standing by this lamppost
on the watch for Sneaky Sue,
if I do not see her shortly,
we are finished, we are through,
our private game of hide-and-seek
began a month ago,
so far I haven't found her,
though I've hunted high and low.

I started out by scouting
every building on the block,
I checked inside our clubhouse,
and behind her special rock,
I rummaged through the bushes,
but I couldn't find a clue,
I climbed a tree for nothing—
not a sign of Sneaky Sue.

I covered every corner
of the lot where little grows,
I peered into the garbage cans
and had to hold my nose,
I searched the haunted cellar
where I'd never been before,
it made me sort of nervous—
I heard murmurs on the floor.

I poked through every alley,
and I peeked in every nook,
I have gotten quite disgusted,
for there's nowhere left to look,
so I'm standing by this lamppost
in our game of hide-and-seek . . .
"Sneaky Sue, come out of hiding,
I will wait just one more week!"

The Carpenter Rages

The carpenter rages, the carpenter rants,
the carpenter raises a clamor,
it's all on account of the carpenter ants,
who have eaten the carpenter's hammer.

The carpenter bellows, the carpenter screams,
the carpenter clenches his jaw,
for the carpenter ants, in well-organized teams,
have eaten the carpenter's saw.

The carpenter sputters, the carpenter stews,
the carpenter simmers and sizzles,
for the carpenter ants, working swiftly in crews,
have eaten the carpenter's chisels.

The carpenter sits in a heap on the ground,
the carpenter grows ever madder,
for the carpenter ants, swarming up and around,
have eaten the carpenter's ladder.

The carpenter suddenly leaps in the air,
he writhes in a furious dance,
for those carpenter ants, with incredible flair,
have eaten the carpenter's pants.

We Heard Wally Wail

We heard Wally wail through the whole
     neighborhood,
as his mother whaled Wally as hard as she could,
she made Wally holler, she made Wally whoop,
for what he had spelled in the alphabet soup.

What Nerve You've Got, Minerva Mott!

What nerve you've got, Minerva Mott!
You're miserable! You're mean!
I'd like to tie you in a knot
and paint your stomach green.

I wish two tigers and a bear
would chase you up a tree.
Minerva Mott! How could you dare
to name your dog for me?

Dainty Dottie Dee

There's no one as immaculate
as dainty Dottie Dee,
who clearly is the cleanest
that a human being can be,
no sooner does she waken
than she hoses down her bed,
then hurries to the kitchen,
and disinfects the bread.

She spends the morning sweeping
every inch of every room,
when all the floors are spotless,
Dottie polishes the broom,
she mops the walls and ceilings,
she scrubs beneath the rug,
and should a bug meander by,
she tidies up that bug.

Dottie boils the phone and toaster,
Dottie rinses the shampoo,
she waxes the salami,
and she vacuums the stew,
she dusts the cheese and crackers,
and she sponges down the pie,
she lathers the spaghetti,
then hangs it up to dry.

Dottie scours the locks and keyholes,
and she soaps the bathroom scale,
she launders every light bulb,
she bathes the morning mail,
but her oddest habit ever
(and of this there's little doubt),
is washing all the garbage
before she throws it out.

I've Got an Incredible Headache

I've got an incredible headache,
my temples are throbbing with pain,
it feels like a freight train with two locomotives
is chugging about in my brain.
I'm sure I can't stand it much longer,
my skull's being squeezed in a vise,
as regiments march to the blaring of trumpets,
and thousands of tap-dancing mice.

My head's filled with horrible noises,
there's a man mashing melons inside,
someone keeps drumming on bongos and plumbing,
as porpoises thrash in the tide.
An elephant herd is stampeding,
a volcano is blowing its top,
and if I keep hitting my head with this hammer,
I doubt that my headache will stop.

Ounce and Bounce

Bowen Ounce and Owen Bounce
fell off a speeding train,
both were rather fortunate,
and lived to fall again.

Owen Bounce, who weighed an ounce,
was cushioned by soft shrubbery,
Bowen Ounce just bounced and bounced,
for he was round and rubbery.

Bleezer's Ice Cream

I am Ebenezer Bleezer,
I run BLEEZER'S ICE CREAM STORE,
there are flavors in my freezer
you have never seen before,
twenty-eight divine creations
too delicious to resist,
why not do yourself a favor,
try the flavors on my list:

COCOA MOCHA MACARONI

TAPIOCA SMOKED BALONEY

CHECKERBERRY CHEDDAR CHEW

CHICKEN CHERRY HONEYDEW

TUTTI-FRUTTI STEWED TOMATO

TUNA TACO BAKED POTATO

LOBSTER LITCHI LIMA BEAN

MOZZARELLA MANGOSTEEN

ALMOND HAM MERINGUE SALAMI

YAM ANCHOVY PRUNE PASTRAMI

SASSAFRAS SOUVLAKI HASH

SUKIYAKI SUCCOTASH

BUTTER BRICKLE PEPPER PICKLE

POMEGRANATE PUMPERNICKEL

PEACH PIMENTO PIZZA PLUM

PEANUT PUMPKIN BUBBLEGUM

BROCCOLI BANANA BLUSTER

CHOCOLATE CHOP SUEY CLUSTER

AVOCADO BRUSSELS SPROUT

PERIWINKLE SAUERKRAUT

COTTON CANDY CARROT CUSTARD

CAULIFLOWER COLA MUSTARD

ONION DUMPLING DOUBLE DIP

TURNIP TRUFFLE TRIPLE FLIP

GARLIC GUMBO GRAVY GUAVA

LENTIL LEMON LIVER LAVA

ORANGE OLIVE BAGEL BEET

WATERMELON WAFFLE WHEAT

I am Ebenezer Bleezer,
I run BLEEZER'S ICE CREAM STORE,
taste a flavor from my freezer,
you will surely ask for more.

Henrietta Snetter

Henrietta Snetter knit a sweater in the night,
in a nutty, neat, and novel sort of way,
for she knit it from the sheep
that she counted in her sleep,
and she wore it when she rose to greet the day.

A Cow's Outside

A cow's outside is mainly hide,
undoubtedly this leather
retains a cow's insides inside,
and holds a cow together.

The Flotz

I am the Flotz, I gobble dots,
indeed, I gobble lots and lots,
every dot I ever see
is bound to be a bite for me.
I often munch on myriads
of sweet, abundant periods,
I nibble hyphens, and with ease
chew succulent apostrophes.

From time to time, I turn my gaze
to little dotted "i's" and "j's,"
and if I chance upon a dash,
I soon dispatch it with panache.
I chomp on commas half the day,
quotation marks are rarer prey,
a semicolon's quite a treat,
while polka dots are joys to eat.

When I confront a dotted line,
my tongue flicks out, those dots are mine,
Morse code becomes a feast, and yes,
I've snacked upon an S.O.S.
For I'm the Flotz, who gobbles dots,
I gobble them in pails and pots,
and you'll not like my brief embrace
if you have freckles on your face.

Homework! Oh, Homework!

Homework! Oh, homework!
I hate you! You stink!
I wish I could wash you
away in the sink,
if only a bomb
would explode you to bits.
Homework! Oh, homework!
You're giving me fits.

I'd rather take baths
with a man-eating shark,
or wrestle a lion
alone in the dark,
eat spinach and liver,
pet ten porcupines,
than tackle the homework
my teacher assigns.

Homework! Oh, homework!
You're last on my list,
I simply can't see
why you even exist,
if you just disappeared
it would tickle me pink.
Homework! Oh, homework!
I hate you! You stink!

Bulgy Bunne

Bulgy Bunne (the wonder builder)
built a boat of brass and wood,
Bulgy chose the finest lumber,
and the brass was just as good.
Every plank he picked was perfect,
there was not a knot in one,
for the best was barely suited
to the boat of Bulgy Bunne.

Bulgy scraped and sawed and sanded,
chiseled, hammered, planed, and drilled,
as he built the grandest sailboat
it was possible to build.
Bulgy buffed and Bulgy burnished,
Bulgy raised a sturdy mast,
Bulgy stitched the strongest fabrics
into sails designed to last.

When his work was finally finished,
Bulgy studied it with pride,
for he knew his stalwart sailboat
was prepared to face the tide.
Bulgy Bunne made but one blunder,
Bulgy's boat will not leave shore,
Bulgy built it in his bedroom
. . . it won't fit through Bulgy's door.

Song of the Gloopy Gloppers

We are Gloppers, gloopy Gloppers,
mucilaginous, gelatinous,
we never fail to find a frail
yet filling form to fatten us,
we ooze about the countryside,
through hamlet and metropolis,
for Gloppers ooze where Gloppers choose,
enveloping the populace.

We are Gloppers, gloopy Gloppers,
unrelenting, irresistible,
what we will do to you is too
distressing to be listable,
we'll ooze into your living room,
your kitchen, and your vestibule,
and in your bed we'll taste your head,
to test if you're digestible.

We are Gloppers, gloopy Gloppers,
globs of undulating Glopper ooze,
you cannot quell our viscid swell,
there is no way to stop our ooze,
for Gloppers are invincible,
unquenchable, unstoppable,
and when we swarm upon *your* form,
we know we'll find you GLOPPABLE!

Stringbean Small

Stringbean Small was tall and trim,
basketball seemed meant for him,
at eight foot four, a coach's dream,
and yet he failed to make the team.

It seems at practice, Stringbean Small
began to chew the basketball,
the coach screamed, "Stop! Don't nibble it!
I wanted you to *dribble* it!"

My Baby Brother

My baby brother is so small,
he hasn't even learned to crawl.
He's only been around a week,
and all he seems to do is bawl
and wiggle, sleep . . . and leak.

My Dog, He Is an Ugly Dog

My dog, he is an ugly dog,
he's put together wrong,
his legs are much too short for him,
his ears are much too long.
My dog, he is a scruffy dog,
he's missing clumps of hair,
his face is quite ridiculous,
his tail is scarcely there.

My dog, he is a dingy dog,
his fur is full of fleas,
he sometimes smells like dirty socks,
he sometimes smells like cheese.
My dog, he is a noisy dog,
he's hardly ever still,
he barks at almost anything,
his voice is loud and shrill.

My dog, he is a stupid dog,
his mind is slow and thick,
he's never learned to catch a ball,
he cannot fetch a stick.
My dog, he is a greedy dog,
he eats enough for three,
his belly bulges to the ground,
he is the dog for me.

Be Glad Your Nose Is on Your Face

Be glad your nose is on your face,
not pasted on some other place,
for if it were where it is not,
you might dislike your nose a lot.

Imagine if your precious nose
were sandwiched in between your toes,
that clearly would not be a treat,
for you'd be forced to smell your feet.

Your nose would be a source of dread
were it attached atop your head,
it soon would drive you to despair,
forever tickled by your hair.

Within your ear, your nose would be
an absolute catastrophe,
for when you were obliged to sneeze,
your brain would rattle from the breeze.

Your nose, instead, through thick and thin,
remains between your eyes and chin,
not pasted on some other place—
be glad your nose is on your face!

Mean Maxine

There's no one mean as mean Maxine,
she smells like old cigars,
her brain is smaller than a bean,
I wish she'd move to Mars.

Some day I'll list the things I hate,
and that is where I'll list her,
I'd like to pack her in a crate—
too bad Maxine's my sister.

We Each Wore Half a Horse

We each wore half a horse,
and pranced in a parade,
and you can guess, of course,
which half of it *I* played.

Yubbazubbies

Yubbazubbies, you are yummy,
you are succulent and sweet,
you are splendidly delicious,
quite delectable to eat,
how I smack my lips with relish
when you bump against my knees,
then nuzzle up beside me,
chirping, "Eat us if you please!"

You are juicy, Yubbazubbies,
you are tender, never tough,
you are appetizing morsels,
I can never get enough,
you have captivating flavors
and a tantalizing smell,
a bit like candied apple,
and a bit like caramel.

Yubbazubbies, you are luscious,
you are soft and smooth as silk,
like a dish of chicken dumplings,
or a glass of chocolate milk,
even when I'm hardly hungry,
I am sure to taste a few,
and I'm never disappointed,
Yubbazubbies, I love you.

Dauntless Dimble

Dauntless Dimble was the bravest
of the bravest of the brave,
Dimble climbed the highest mountain,
he explored the deepest cave,
Dimble fought the fiercest creatures,
but he never met his match,
Dimble often wrestled tigers
and escaped without a scratch.

Not a challenge went unanswered,
he accepted every dare,
Dimble walked on blazing embers
and was none the worse for wear,
Dimble exited an airplane
high above a rocky butte,
he escaped with minor bruises
though he wore no parachute.

Dimble diving in the ocean
was beset by hungry sharks,
yet the only wounds he suffered
were some superficial marks,
once a polar bear attacked him
on the icy arctic floes,
the result of that adventure
was a slightly bloody nose.

Dimble danced with deadly cobras,
Dimble toyed with killer bees,
Dimble dangled by one finger
from a tiny greased trapeze,
but he rose from sleep one morning,
and while getting out of bed,
Dimble tripped upon the carpet,
where he cracked his dauntless head.

I Spied My Shadow Slinking

I spied my shadow slinking
up behind me in the night,
I issued it a challenge,
and we started in to fight.

I wrestled with that shadow,
but it wasn't any fun,
I tried my very hardest—
all the same, my shadow won.

Today Is a Day to Crow About

Today is a day to crow about,
it's a crowable sort of day,
for the crows have frightened the scarecrow,
and the scarecrow is running away.

I Found a Four-Leaf Clover

I found a four-leaf clover
and was happy with my find,
but with time to think it over,
I've entirely changed my mind.
I concealed it in my pocket,
safe inside a paper pad,
soon, much swifter than a rocket,
my good fortune turned to bad.

I smashed my fingers in a door,
I dropped a dozen eggs,
I slipped and tumbled to the floor,
a dog nipped both my legs,
my ring slid down the bathtub drain,
my pen leaked on my shirt,
I barked my shin, I missed my train,
I sat on my dessert.

I broke my brand-new glasses,
and I couldn't find my keys,
I stepped in spilled molasses,
and was stung by angry bees.
When the kitten ripped the curtain,
and the toast burst into flame,
I was absolutely certain
that the clover was to blame.

I buried it discreetly
in the middle of a field,
now my luck has changed completely,
and my wounds have almost healed.
If I ever find another,
I will simply let it be,
or I'll give it to my brother—
he deserves it more than me.

Gussie's Greasy Spoon

Every day, at ten past noon,
I enter GUSSIE'S GREASY SPOON,
I plop down in the nearest seat,
and order food unfit to eat.
I try the juice, it's warm and vile,
the scrambled eggs are green as bile,
the beets are blue, the beans are gray,
the cauliflower tastes like clay.

At GUSSIE'S GREASY SPOON, the stew
is part cement, part hay, part glue,
it's mostly gristle, ropy tough,
a tiger couldn't chew the stuff.
The rancid soup is foul and thin,
a bit like bitter medicine,
the melon smells, the salad sags,
the mashed potatoes seem like rags.

One whiff of Gussie's weird cuisine
makes stomachs ache, turns faces green,
her moldy muffins have no peers,
they'll make you sick for forty years.
The coffee's cold, the cake is stale,
the doughnuts taste like pickled whale,
yet, every day, at ten past noon,
I eat at GUSSIE'S GREASY SPOON.

New York Is in North Carolina

New York is in North Carolina.
Seattle is found in Peru.
New Mexico borders on Norway and Italy.
Boston's near Kalamazoo.
Quebec is a town in Hawaii.
Connecticut lies in Trieste.

Those are a few of the answers I wrote
when I flunked the geography test.

Super-Goopy Glue

Permit me to present to you
my famous SUPER-GOOPY GLUE,
by far the finest glue on earth,
one dollar for a penny's worth.

It's rumored that my glue adheres
for easily a thousand years,
my glue's the glue you surely seek,
it's guaranteed for one whole week.

My SUPER-GOOPY GLUE can glue
a carrot to a caribou,
a feather to a ferret's feet,
a pickle to a parakeet.

No other glue is half as good,
it works on metal, glass, and wood,
I'd demonstrate it for you, but
my glue has glued my gluepot shut.

The Cherries' Garden Gala

The Cherries' garden gala
was the finest seen in years,
the Pears arrived in couples,
and the Prunes all carried shears,
the Greens had splendid collars,
and the Peaches wore new shoes,
an Orange danced a hornpipe,
and a Berry sang the blues.

The Beets were playing bongos,
as the Lettuce marched ahead,
the Zucchini made a racket,
but the Ginger seemed well-bred,
the Dates appeared unsteady,
though the Currants stayed on course,
the Turnips whirled in circles,
and the Radishes grew hoarse.

The Beans could not stop coughing
as the Corn told awful jokes,
the Plums were bobbing gaily
with some hearty Artichokes,
a Cauliflower listened
as the Grapes began to whine,
and the Melons started bawling
just to see the Apples pine.

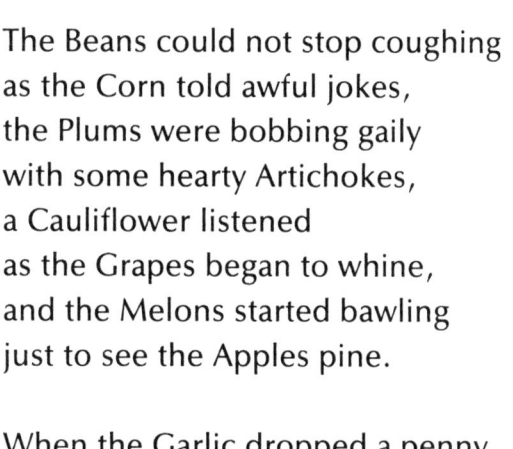

When the Garlic dropped a penny
and the Mint produced a bill,
the Chard grew overheated,
and a Pepper caught a chill,
then the Rhubarb got to fighting,
and the Lemons seemed afraid,
but the Thyme could not help watching,
though the Mushrooms all sought aid.

The Onions dipped politely,
as the Leeks began to spring,
the Sage repeated maxims,
and the Carrots formed a ring,
a Tomato acted saucy
to a rather bossy Pea,
and Potatoes wept with pleasure
at the Cherries' jubilee.

An Alley Cat with One Life Left

I'm an alley cat with one life left,
I started out with nine,
but lost the first in a knockdown fight
with a cat named Frankenstein,
my second went soon after that
to something that I ate,
my third went under a garbage truck—
I noticed it too late.

While strolling through the zoo one day,
I heard an awful roar,
I'd strayed into a lion's cage—
so much for number four,
I lost my fifth one morning
to a ton of falling bricks,
then tumbled from a window ledge,
and gave up number six.

My seventh went to a Saint Bernard—
I was no match for him,
my eighth was squandered in the lake—
it seems I couldn't swim,
so now I'd better watch my step,
I'm down to number nine,
I'm an alley cat with one life left,
and glad that life is mine.

An Irritating Creature

There's an irritating creature
in my living room today,
it's been here for a year now,
and it will not go away.
The first time that I saw it,
it was in my easy chair,
and displayed no inclination
to forsake its station there.

I put it in a parcel,
and I left it at the store,
the thing was there to greet me
when I opened up my door,
I took it to the forest,
and I tied it to a tree,
I found it in my kitchen
having sandwiches and tea.

I packed it in a carton
to disguise its size and shape,
I wrapped it and I stamped it
and I sealed it shut with tape,
I mailed it to the middle
of a mountain in Tibet,
I returned to see it sitting
on my brand-new TV set.

I concealed it in a rocket
that was bound for outer space,
it was back that very evening
with a smile upon its face.
It appears I can't evict it,
though I truly wish I could,
it's entirely too tenacious—
I suspect it's here for good.

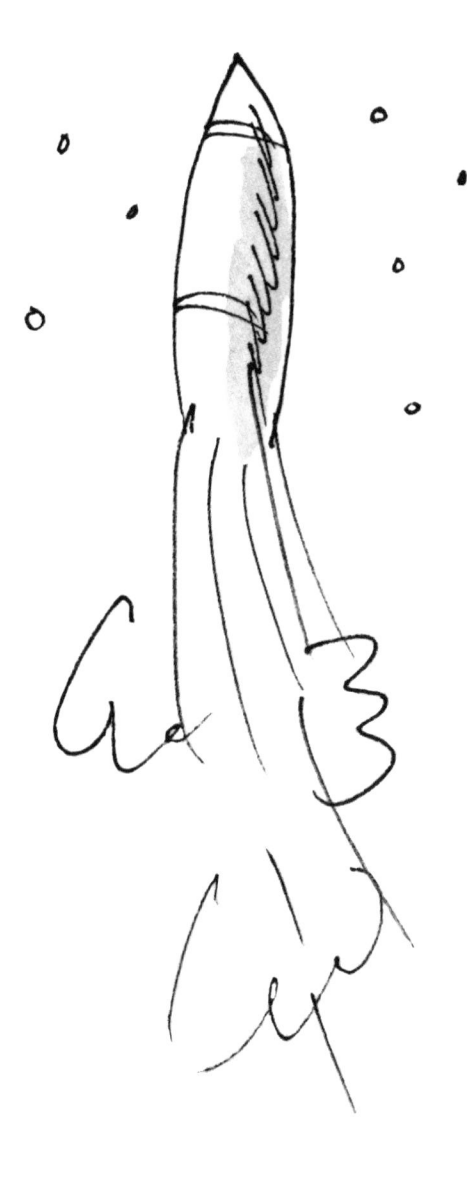

Sir Blushington Bloone

Sir Blushington Bloone is a knight of the court,
with a face like a prune of the large, wrinkled sort,
he's a very odd bird, with a mind of his own,
who is frequently heard singing songs to a stone.

He's a singular lord, with a singular head,
he carries no sword, but a yo-yo instead,
he sometimes sips soup from a small, slotted spoon,
while rolling a hoop to a baffled raccoon.

Sir Blushington Bloone often goes for a ride
in a silver balloon, with a pig by his side,
and there he shampoos his immaculate wig,
while discussing the news of the day with the pig.

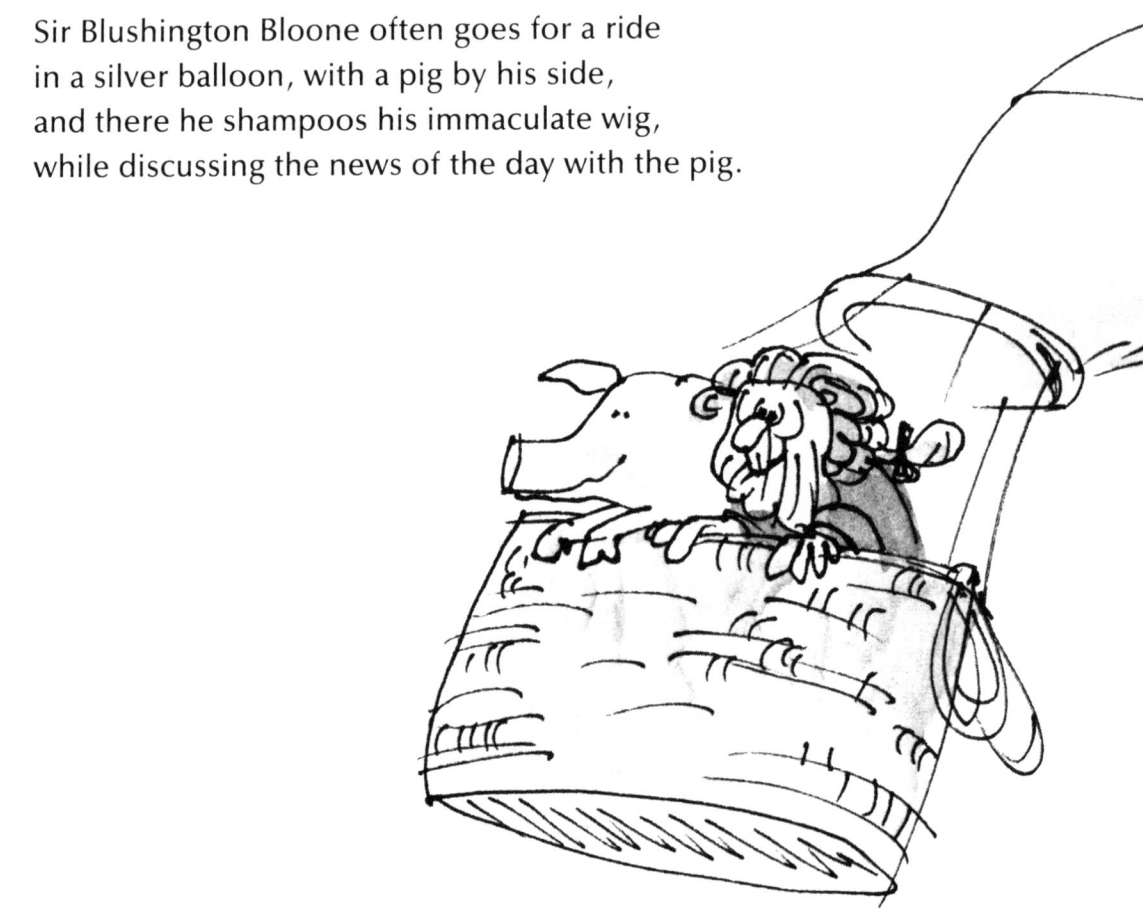

By the light of the moon, wearing little or less,
he sits with a loon for an evening of chess,
or waves his baton as he slogs through the bogs,
conducting a swan and a chorus of frogs.

He's been seen on the green on the tips of his toes
as he balances beans on the end of his nose,
he flies kites from his ears every Tuesday at noon,
oh, a knight with no peers is Sir Blushington Bloone.

When Tillie Ate the Chili

When Tillie ate the chili,
she erupted from her seat,
she gulped a quart of water,
and fled screaming down the street,
she coughed, she wheezed, she sputtered,
she ran totally amok,
she set a new world record
as she raced around the block.

Tillie's mouth was full of fire,
Tillie's eyes were red with tears,
she was smoking from her nostrils,
she was steaming from her ears,
she cooled off an hour later,
showing perfect self-control
as she said, "What tasty chili,
I should like another bowl."

Never Mince Words with a Shark

You may quarrel with centipedes, quibble with seals,
declaim to a duck in the park,
engage in disputes with cantankerous coots,
but never mince words with a shark.

You may rant at an anteater, banter with eels,
and haggle with gaggles of geese,
heap verbal abuse on a monkey or moose,
but a shark you had best leave in peace.

You may argue with otters, make speeches to teals,
and lecture at length to a shrew,
but a shark will deflate your attempts at debate,
and before you are done, you are through.

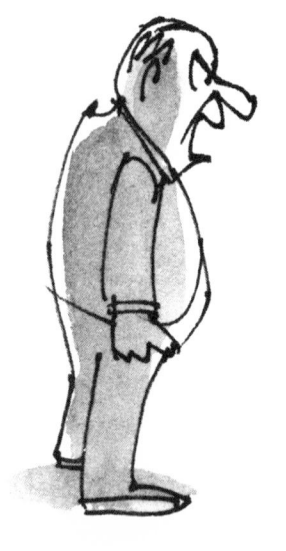

I Am Flying!

I am flying! I am flying!
I am riding on the breeze,
I am soaring over meadows,
I am sailing over seas,
I ascend above the cities
where the people, small as ants,
cannot sense the keen precision
of my aerobatic dance.

I am flying! I am flying!
I am climbing unconfined,
I am swifter than the falcon,
and I leave the wind behind,
I am swooping, I am swirling
in a jubilant display,
I am brilliant as a comet
blazing through the Milky Way.

I am flying! I am flying!
I am higher than the moon,
still, I think I'd best be landing,
and it cannot be too soon,
for some nasty information
has lit up my little brain—
I am flying! I am flying!
but I fly without a plane.

The Mungle and the Munn

The duo met to duel at dawn
(the Mungle and the Munn),
to settle certain matters,
as indeed they'd often done.
The Munn struck first and tweaked a cheek,
but being tweaked right back,
detached the Mungle's tender tail,
and dropped it in a sack.

The Mungle dashed his mallet
on his foe's defenseless toes,
the Munn produced his pliers
and removed his rival's nose.
The Mungle, somewhat angered,
gnawed his adversary's ear,
the Munn undid the Mungle's horn,
the Mungle shed a tear.

The contest grew intenser,
and the Mungle, seeing red,
took soap and blade and neatly shaved
the Munn's unguarded head.
They struggled for position,
they attacked with perfect aim,
whatever deed the Mungle did,
the Munn did much the same.

They battled on with cantaloupes,
with sandwiches and snips,
with kegs of pegs, with rotten eggs,
with prunes and paper clips.
At noon the duelists drew apart
(the Mungle and the Munn),
they bowed and said, "Let's meet again—
it's certainly been fun!"

Throckmorton Thratte

Throckmorton Thratte has charm and class,
he's wealthy and he's handsome,
small wonder that his looking glass
is holding him for ransom.

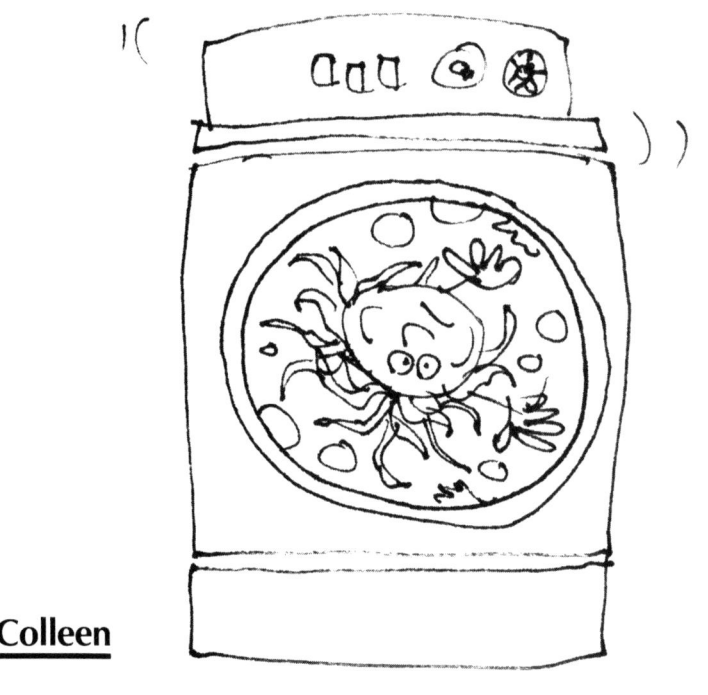

Uncanny Colleen

Uncanny Colleen (unaccountably green)
is munching on cabbage and squash,
while spinning around in her washing machine—
no doubt she'll come out in the wash.

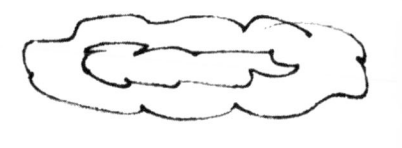

Today Is Very Boring

Today is very boring,
it's a very boring day,
there is nothing much to look at,
there is nothing much to say,
there's a peacock on my sneakers,
there's a penguin on my head,
there's a dormouse on my doorstep,
I am going back to bed.

Today is very boring,
it is boring through and through,
there is absolutely nothing
that I think I want to do,
I see giants riding rhinos,
and an ogre with a sword,
there's a dragon blowing smoke rings,
I am positively bored.

Today is very boring,
I can hardly help but yawn,
there's a flying saucer landing
in the middle of my lawn,
a volcano just erupted
less than half a mile away,
and I think I felt an earthquake,
it's a very boring day.

Griselda Gratz

Griselda Gratz kept sixty cats,
she fed them very well
on angel cakes and raisin flakes
and acorns in a shell.

Her furry crowd patrolled, meowed
about her tiny house,
Griselda Gratz kept sixty cats,
to catch a single mouse.

I Toss Them to My Elephant

When the summer sun is blazing,
I pick daisy after daisy,
I toss them to my elephant—
it makes him slightly crazy.

I gather up chrysanthemums
when fall is in the air,
I toss them to my elephant—
it makes him stand and stare.

I harvest bright poinsettias
in winter, when it's chilly,
I toss them to my elephant—
it makes him sort of silly.

I pluck bouquets of tulips
when they blossom in the spring,
I toss them to my elephant . . .
it always makes him sing!

A Microscopic Topic

I am a paramecium
that cannot do a simple sum,
and it's a rather well-known fact
I'm quite unable to subtract.

If I'd an eye, I'd surely cry
about the way I multiply,
for though I've often tried and tried,
I do it backward . . . and divide.

My Brother's Head Should Be Replaced

My brother's head should be replaced,
it's lighter than a feather,
he's trying to use tomato paste
to paste tomatoes together.

Michael Built a Bicycle

Michael built a bicycle
unsuitable for speed,
it's crammed with more accessories
than anyone could need,
there's an AM-FM radio,
a deck to play cassettes,
a refrigerator-freezer,
and a pair of TV sets.

There are shelves for shirts and sweaters,
there are hangers for his jeans,
a drawer for socks and underwear,
a rack for magazines,
there's a fishtank and a birdcage
perched upon the handlebars,
a bookcase, and a telescope
to watch the moon and stars.

There's a telephone, a blender,
and a stove to cook his meals,
there's a sink to do the dishes
somehow fastened to the wheels,
there's a portable piano,
and a set of model trains,
an automatic bumbershoot
that opens when it rains.

There's a desk for typing letters
on his fabulous machine,
a stall for taking showers,
and a broom to keep things clean,
but you'll never see him ride it,
for it isn't quite complete,
Michael left no room for pedals,
and there isn't any seat.

Eggs!

Eggs!
You're excellent, exquisite,
I exalt you, hot or cold,
I salute you in a salad,
I commend you in a mold,
you are scrumptious lightly scrambled,
fully fascinating fried,
incandescent over easy,
dazzling on your sunny side.

Eggs!
You're dainty when you're coddled,
when you're stuffed, I long to bite,
you're angelic when you're deviled,
when you're shirred, you're sheer delight,
you are magic on a muffin,
gold ambrosia on a bun,
you are princely, poached precisely,
when your yellow starts to run.

Eggs!
You're nectar in an omelette,
in soufflés, a savory dream,
baked or boiled you are bewitching,
in a quiche, you reign supreme,
yes, I love you to distraction,
but alas, you have a flaw,
for you're thoroughly revolting
when you're swallowed whole and raw.

The Flimsy Fleek

The flimsy Fleek is mild and meek,
its teeth are dull, its jaws are weak,
it has a fragile, frail physique,
its limbs are lean and little.
Its neck is short, its face is pale,
its lips are thin, its breath is stale,
it has a twist of tufted tail,
its bones are bent and brittle.

It lives beneath a bumbershoot,
it nibbles twigs and bits of fruit,
it only wears its birthday suit,
its skin is thick with wrinkles.
Its ears resemble dinner rolls,
its nose is but two buttonholes,
its eyes are large as salad bowls,
they teem with tiny twinkles.

The Fleek is quite content to dwell
within its share of shady dell,
attempting to subtract and spell,
it is, I fear, not clever.
If you should find this flimsy Fleek,
and are so foolish as to speak,
the Fleek will squeak, and in a streak,
will disappear forever.

Floradora Doe

Consider the calamity
of Floradora Doe,
who talked to all her plants, because
she thought it helped them grow,
she recited to her ivy,
to her fennel, ferns, and phlox,
she chatted with her cacti
in their little window box.

She murmured to her mosses,
and she yammered to her yew,
she babbled to her basil,
to her borage and bamboo,
she lectured to her laurels,
to her lilac and her lime,
she whispered to her willows,
and she tittered to her thyme.

She gossiped with a poppy,
and she prattled to a rose,
she regaled her rhododendrons
with a constant stream of prose,
then suddenly, one morning,
every plant keeled over, dead.
"Alas!" moaned Floradora.
"Was it something that I said?"

Oh, Teddy Bear

Oh, Teddy Bear, dear Teddy,
though you're gone these many years,
I recall with deep affection
how I nibbled on your ears,
I can hardly keep from smiling,
and my heart beats fast and glows,
when I think about the morning
that I twisted off your nose.

Teddy Bear, you didn't whimper,
Teddy Bear, you didn't pout,
when I reached in with my fingers
and I tore your tummy out,
and you didn't even mumble
or emit the faintest cries,
when I pulled your little paws off,
when I bit your button eyes.

Yes, you sat beside me calmly,
and you didn't once protest,
when I ripped apart the stuffing
that was packed inside your chest,
and you didn't seem to notice
when I yanked out all your hair—
it's been ages since I've seen you,
but I miss you, Teddy Bear.

My Mother Says I'm Sickening

My mother says I'm sickening,
my mother says I'm crude,
she says this when she sees me
playing Ping-Pong with my food,
she doesn't seem to like it
when I slurp my bowl of stew,
and now she's got a list of things
she says I mustn't do—

DO NOT CATAPULT THE CARROTS!

DO NOT JUGGLE GOBS OF FAT!

DO NOT DROP THE MASHED POTATOES

ON THE GERBIL OR THE CAT!

NEVER PUNCH THE PUMPKIN PUDDING!

NEVER TUNNEL THROUGH THE BREAD!

PUT NO PEAS INTO YOUR POCKET!

PLACE NO NOODLES ON YOUR HEAD!

DO NOT SQUEEZE THE STEAMED ZUCCHINI!

DO NOT MAKE THE MELON OOZE!

NEVER STUFF VANILLA YOGURT

IN YOUR LITTLE SISTER'S SHOES!

DRAW NO FACES IN THE KETCHUP!

MAKE NO LITTLE GRAVY POOLS!

I wish my mother wouldn't make
so many useless rules.

When Dracula Went to the Blood Bank

When Dracula went to the blood bank,
he thoroughly flustered the staff,
for rather than make a donation,
he drew out a pint and a half.

When Young, the Slyne

When young, the Slyne, from noon to nine,
stood blithely on its head,
and rudely chewed on thread and twine,
"How odd!" I often said.

The Slyne, now grown, chews yet on thread
and twine, from noon to nine,
but does not stand upon its head,
it stands, instead, on mine.

Ballad of a Boneless Chicken

I'm a basic boneless chicken,
yes, I have no bones inside,
I'm without a trace of rib cage,
yet I hold myself with pride,
other hens appear offended
by my total lack of bones,
they discuss me impolitely
in derogatory tones.

I am absolutely boneless,
I am boneless through and through,
I have neither neck nor thighbones,
and my back is boneless too,
and I haven't got a wishbone,
not a bone within my breast,
so I rarely care to travel
from the comfort of my nest.

I have feathers fine and fluffy,
I have lovely little wings,
but I lack the superstructure
to support these splendid things.
Since a chicken finds it tricky
to parade on boneless legs,
I stick closely to the hen house,
laying little scrambled eggs.

Seymour Snorkke

"With chopsticks did I sip my soup,"
  so stated Seymour Snorkke,
"but that was much too difficult,
  so now I use a fork."

There Is a Thing

There is a thing
beneath the stair
with slimy face
and oily hair
that does not move
or speak or sing
or do another
single thing
but sit and wait
beneath the stair
with slimy face
and oily hair.

Ma! Don't Throw That Shirt Out

Ma! Don't throw that shirt out,
it's my all-time favorite shirt!
I admit it smells peculiar,
and is stained with grease and dirt,
that it's missing half its buttons,
and has got so many holes
that it might have been infested
by a regiment of moles.

Yes! I know that I've outgrown it,
that it's faded and it's torn,
I can see the sleeves are frazzled,
I'm aware the collar's worn,
but I've had that shirt forever,
and I swear that I'll be hurt
if you dare to throw that shirt out—
IT'S MY ALL-TIME FAVORITE SHIRT!

Suzanna Socked Me Sunday

Suzanna socked me Sunday,
she socked me Monday, too,
she also socked me Tuesday,
I was turning black and blue.

She socked me double Wednesday,
and Thursday even more,
but when she socked me Friday,
she began to get me sore.

"Enough's enough," I yelled at her,
"I hate it when you hit me!"
"Well, then I won't!" Suzanna said—
   that Saturday, she bit me.

The Zoosher

Beneath a bush, the Zoosher lies,
with mashed potatoes on its eyes,
with fried zucchini in its nose,
with carrot sticks between its toes.
Impaled upon its single horn
are toasted ears of baby corn,
and on its chest, it wears no less
than rhubarb, ringed with watercress.

The Zoosher keeps in either paw
a pair of leeks, one cooked, one raw,
an eggplant dangles from its beard
(some find this practice rather weird).
Assembled neatly on its knees
are little pods of early peas,
while resting boldly on its thighs
are yams of more than average size.

It's hard to fault the Zoosher's taste
(a mushroom belt adorns its waist),
and gaily wrapped about its head
are radishes—some white, some red.
Just why the beast behaves this way
is rather difficult to say,
as here beneath a bush it lies,
with mashed potatoes on its eyes.

I'd Never Eat a Beet

I'd never eat a beet, because
I could not stand the taste,
I'd rather nibble drinking straws,
or fountain pens, or paste,
I'd eat a window curtain
and perhaps a roller skate,
but a beet, you may be certain
would be wasted on my plate.

I would sooner chew on candles
or the laces from my shoes,
or a dozen suitcase handles
were I ever forced to choose,
I would eat a Ping-Pong paddle,
I would eat a Ping-Pong ball,
I might even eat a saddle,
but a beet? No! Not at all.

I would swallow talcum powder
and my little rubber duck,
I'd have doorknobs in my chowder,
I would eat a hockey puck,
I would eat my model rocket
and the socks right off my feet,
I would even eat my pocket,
but I'd never eat a beet!

Boing! Boing! Squeak!

Boing! Boing! Squeak!
Boing! Boing! Squeak!
A bouncing mouse is in my house,
it's been here for a week.

It bounced from out of nowhere,
then quickly settled in,
I'm grateful that it came alone
(I've heard it has a twin),
it bounces in the kitchen,
it bounces in the den,
it bounces through the living room—
look! There it goes again.

Boing! Boing! Squeak!
Boing! Boing! Squeak!
A bouncing mouse is in my house,
it's been here for a week.

It bounces on the sofa,
on the table and the bed,
up the stairs and on the chairs
and even on my head,
that mouse continues bouncing
every minute of the day,
it bounces, bounces, bounces,
but it doesn't bounce away.

Boing! Boing! Squeak!
Boing! Boing! Squeak!
A bouncing mouse is in my house,
it's been here for a week.

I'm Disgusted with My Brother

I'm disgusted with my brother,
I am positively sore,
I have never been so angry
with a human being before,
he's everything detestable
that's spelled with A through Z,
he deserves to be the target
of a ten-pound bumblebee.

I'd like to wave a magic wand
and make him disappear,
or watch a wild rhinoceros
attack him from the rear,
perhaps I'll cook a pot of soup
and dump my brother in,
he forgot today's my birthday—
oh, how could he . . . he's my *twin!*

Dora Diller

"My stomach's full of butterflies!"
lamented Dora Diller.
Her mother sighed. "That's no surprise,
you ate a caterpillar!"

Lavinia Nink

Lavinia Nink lives serenely
in a house unmistakably rare,
for the water turns on in the shower
when Lavinia sits in a chair,
when she opens the door to the freezer,
the clock strikes a quarter to ten,
and as soon as she starts up the oven,
the telephone rings in the den.

When Lavinia plays the piano,
the toaster repeatedly pops,
and the TV keeps changing the channel
whenever Lavinia mops,
all the lights in the living room flicker
when she washes her hands in the sink,
it's a house to drive anyone nutty,
but it's home to Lavinia Nink.

I Do Not Like the Rat!

I praise the hippopotamus,
I celebrate the bat,
I hold the bream in high esteem—
I DO NOT LIKE THE RAT!

I cotton to the octopus,
I tolerate the gnat,
I dote upon the stately swan—
I SHUDDER AT THE RAT!

I value the rhinoceros,
I venerate the cat,
I quite salute the simple newt—
I CANNOT STAND THE RAT!

The Diatonic Dittymunch

The Diatonic Dittymunch
plucked music from the air,
it swallowed scores of symphonies,
and still had space to spare,
sonatas and cantatas
slithered sweetly down its throat,
it made ballads into salads,
and consumed them note by note.

It ate marches and mazurkas,
it ate rhapsodies and reels,
minuets and tarantellas
were the staples of its meals,
but the Diatonic Dittymunch
outdid itself one day,
it ate a three-act opera,
and loudly passed away.

I'm Bold, I'm Brave

I'm bold, I'm brave, I know no fear.
I'm gallant as a buccaneer.
Is that a hornet by my ear?
Gangway! I'm getting out of here!

Baloney Belly Billy

Baloney Belly Billy
swallows anything for cash,
if you offer him a penny,
he'll chew paper from the trash,
he'll eat guppies for a nickel,
for a dime, he'll eat a bug,
and a quarter will convince him
that he ought to eat a slug.

I have seen him eat a button,
I have seen him eat a bee,
I have seen him eat three beetles
for a half a dollar fee,
for a dollar he will gladly
eat a lizard off a fence,
just imagine what he'd swallow
for another fifty cents.

Come See the Thing

Come see the thing that Dad has caught—
oh, yuck! . . . don't even bother,
it is not dead as Dad had thought,
and we are minus Father.

The Nothing-Doings

Meet the lazy Nothing-Doings,
all they do is stand around,
when it's time for doing nothing,
Nothing-Doings can be found,
when it's time for doing something,
you won't find a single one,
for the Nothing-Doings vanish
when there's work that must be done.

I'm the Single Most Wonderful Person I Know

I'm the single most wonderful person I know,
I'm witty, I'm charming, I'm smart,
I'm often so brilliant I actually glow,
I'm a genius in music and art.

I'm super, I'm splendid, I'm stunning, I'm strong,
I'm awesome, I'm dashing, I'm bold,
I know all the answers, it's rare that I'm wrong,
I'm an absolute joy to behold.

I'm strikingly handsome, I'm thoroughly grand,
I'm uncategorically clever,
there's only one thing that I can't understand—
why nobody likes me . . . not ever!

My Sister Is a Sissy

My sister is a sissy,
she's afraid of dogs and cats,
a toad can give her tantrums,
and she's terrified of rats,
she screams at things with stingers,
things that buzz, and things that crawl,
just the shadow of a spider
sends my sister up the wall.

A lizard makes her shiver,
and a turtle makes her squirm,
she positively cringes
at the prospect of a worm,
she's afraid of things with feathers,
she's afraid of things with fur,
she's scared of almost everything—
how come I'm scared of her?

Miraculous Mortimer

Miraculous Mortimer (Master Magician)
has sawn his assistant in two.
He can't recall how to reverse her condition—
has anyone here any glue?

The Cave Beast Greets a Visitor

Ah! Welcome to my chamber,
do step in and stay awhile,
I so rarely host a stranger
in this humble domicile.
You're unquestionably weary,
and could use a bit of rest,
it's my joy to entertain you
as my dearly honored guest.

Undoubtedly you're thirsty,
sip some liquid from this flask,
you appear to have some queries,
I shall answer all you ask.
The skulls within the corner?
The bones within the bin?
Mere decorative trifles—
they were here when I moved in.

My teeth, you say? My talons?
My mandibular expanse?
Quite the ticket for consuming
tender stems of tiny plants.
This blade you see me sharpen?
Let me set your mind at ease—
I find it indispensable
for slicing bread and cheese.

You say you must be going?
Goodness gracious, why the haste?
Dinner simmers on the fire,
you may find it to your taste.
Whet your palate with a spoonful,
it's a most nutritious stew.
What's that? It lacks in savor?
Then I'll flavor it with **YOU!!!**

I'm in a Rotten Mood!

I'm in a rotten mood today,
a really rotten mood today,
I'm feeling cross,
I'm feeling mean,
I'm jumpy as a jumping bean,
I have an awful attitude—
I'M IN A ROTTEN MOOD!

I'm in a rotten mood today,
a really rotten mood today,
I'm in a snit,
I'm in a stew,
there's nothing that I care to do
but sit all by myself and brood—
I'M IN A ROTTEN MOOD!

I'm in a rotten mood today,
a really rotten mood today,
you'd better stay away from me,
I'm just a lump of misery,
I'm feeling absolutely rude—
I'M IN A ROTTEN MOOD!

Something Silky

Something silky, scarcely there,
ghostly and diaphanous,
stole our socks and underwear,
and had a ghastly laugh on us.

Archie B. McCall

The shrewdest salesman anywhere
is Archie B. McCall,
he's king of selling anything
to anyone at all,
Archie's ways are so persuasive
he's been never known to fail,
he has sold a yak a jacket,
sacks of feathers to a snail.

He has sold a fish a hairbrush,
and a snake a pair of shoes,
peddled Pogo sticks and purses
to a troop of kangaroos,
he has sold a camel earmuffs,
and a trumpet to a moose,
a bikini to a beaver,
an umbrella to a goose.

No one ever turns down Archie,
for when Archie's at his best,
he can sell an eagle glasses,
he can sell a worm a vest,
Archie's simply irresistible,
he's matchless, he's a whiz,
he talked *me* into buying *this*—
I wonder what it is.

I'd Never Dine on Dinosaurs

I'd never dine on dinosaurs,
they can't be good to eat,
for all they've got are lots of bones,
and not a bit of meat.

Forty Performing Bananas

We're FORTY PERFORMING BANANAS,
in bright yellow slippery skins,
our features are rather appealing,
though we've neither shoulders nor chins,
we cha-cha, fandango, and tango,
we kick and we skip and we hop,
while half of us belt out a ballad,
the rest of us spin like a top.

We're FORTY PERFORMING BANANAS,
we mambo, we samba, we waltz,
we dangle and swing from the ceiling,
then turn very slick somersaults,
people drive here in bunches to see us,
our splits earn us worldly renown,
we're FORTY PERFORMING BANANAS,
come see us when you are in town.

Sidney Snickke

Serving supper, Sidney Snickke
played a strange and silly trick.

He inserted jumping beans
in his parents' salad greens.

By dessert, his mom and dad
appeared, to Sidney, hopping mad.

I Am Falling off a Mountain

I am falling off a mountain,
I am plummeting through space,
you may see this does not please me
by the frown upon my face.

As the ground keeps getting nearer,
it's a simple task to tell
that I've got a slight dilemma,
that my day's not going well.

My velocity's increasing,
I am dropping like a stone,
I could do with some assistance,
is there someone I can phone?

Though I'm unafraid of falling,
I am prompted to relate
that the landing has me worried,
and I don't have long to wait.

I am running out of options,
there's just one thing left to try—
in the next eleven seconds,
I have got to learn to fly!

Zany Zapper Zockke

The greatest ace of video space
was zany Zapper Zockke,
for just a single quarter
he could play around the clock.
One day he played a fateful game
of **SUPER SPACE SARDINES,**
he loved to zap those fishy blips
to countless smithereens.

They stormed in strange formations
but he boldly beat them back,
with both his blasters blazing,
Zapper weathered each attack.
They employed bizarre maneuvers,
and they set uncanny traps,
yet they met disintegration
from his lightning counter-zaps.

His hands were swift, his aim was true,
his strategy was keen,
he faced those fish invaders,
and he blew them off the screen.
They seemed to swoop from nowhere,
but he calmly kept his wits,
and with sharp and deadly volleys,
Zapper shattered them to bits.

The machine began to sizzle
as the points began to mount,
he zapped so many space sardines
that even *he* lost count.
Then, in a flash, he vanished,
for he moved at such a pace,
that he spun into a time warp—
Zapper Zockke's in hyperspace!

Happy Birthday, Dear Dragon

There were rumbles of strange jubilation
in a dark, subterranean lair,
for the dragon was having a birthday,
and his colleagues were gathering there.
"**HOORAH!**" groaned the trolls and the ogres
as they pelted each other with stones.
"**HOORAH!**" shrieked a sphinx and a griffin,
and the skeletons rattled their bones.

"*HOORAH!*" screamed the queen of the demons.
"**HOORAH!**" boomed a giant. "**REJOICE!**"
"Hoorah!" piped a tiny hobgoblin
in an almost inaudible voice.
"*HOORAH!*" cackled rapturous witches.
"*Hoorahhhhhhh!*" hissed a basilisk too.
Then they howled in cacophonous chorus,
"*HAPPY BIRTHDAY,*
DEAR DRAGON,
TO YOU!"

They whistled, they squawked, they applauded,
as they gleefully brought forth the cake.

"OH, THANK YOU!"

he thundered with pleasure
in a bass that made every ear ache.
Then puffing his chest to the fullest,
and taking deliberate aim,
the dragon huffed once at the candles—

**and
the candles
all burst
into
flame!**

Index to Titles

Ah! A Monster's Lot Is Merry, 34
Alley Cat with One Life Left, An, 82
Alligators Are Unfriendly, 14
Archie B. McCall, 144

Ballad of a Boneless Chicken, 116
Baloney Belly Billy, 134
Be Glad Your Nose Is on Your Face, 64
Bleezer's Ice Cream, 48
Bloders Are Exploding, The, 37
Boing! Boing! Squeak!, 126
Bulgy Bunne, 56

Carpenter Rages, The, 40
Cave Beast Greets a Visitor, The, 140
Cherries' Garden Gala, The, 80
Clara Cleech, 10
Come See the Thing, 135
Cow's Outside, A, 51
Cuckoo!, 19

Dainty Dottie Dee, 44
Dauntless Dimble, 70
Diatonic Dittymunch, The, 132
Do Oysters Sneeze?, 20
Dora Diller, 129
Drumpp the Grump, 12

Eggs!, 104
Euphonica Jarre, 26

Flimsy Fleek, The, 106
Floradora Doe, 108
Flotz, The, 52
Forty Performing Bananas, 147

Granny Grizer, 32
Griselda Gratz, 98
Gussie's Greasy Spoon, 76

Happy Birthday, Dear Dragon, 152
Henrietta Snetter, 50
Homework! Oh, Homework!, 54

I Am Falling off a Mountain, 149
I Am Flying!, 90
I Am Running in a Circle, 18
I Do Not Like the Rat!, 131
I Found a Four-Leaf Clover, 74
I Spied My Shadow Slinking, 72
I Toss Them to My Elephant, 99
I Wonder Why Dad Is So Thoroughly Mad, 11
I'd Never Dine on Dinosaurs, 146
I'd Never Eat a Beet, 124
I'm Bold, I'm Brave, 133
I'm Disgusted with My Brother, 128
I'm in a Rotten Mood!, 142
I'm Thankful, 28
I'm the Single Most Wonderful Person I Know, 137
Irritating Creature, An, 84
Its Fangs Were Red, 22
I've Got an Incredible Headache, 46
I've Got an Itch, 24

Jellyfish Stew, 8

Lavinia Nink, 130
Louder than a Clap of Thunder!, 36

Ma! Don't Throw That Shirt Out, 120
Mabel, Remarkable Mabel, 21
Mean Maxine, 66
Michael Built a Bicycle, 102
Microscopic Topic, A, 100
Miraculous Mortimer, 139
Mungle and the Munn, The, 92
My Baby Brother, 61
My Brother's Head Should Be Replaced, 101
My Dog, He Is an Ugly Dog, 62
My Mother Says I'm Sickening, 112
My Sister Is a Sissy, 138

Neighbors Are Not Fond of Me, The, 33
Never Mince Words with a Shark, 89

New Kid on the Block, The, 7
New York Is in North Carolina, 78
Nine Mice, 9
No, I Won't Turn Orange!, 31
Nothing-Doings, The, 136

Oh, Teddy Bear, 110
Ounce and Bounce, 47

Seymour Snorkke, 118
Sidney Snickke, 148
Sir Blushington Bloone, 86
Sneaky Sue, 38
Snillies, 25
Something Silky, 143
Song of the Gloopy Gloppers, 58
Stringbean Small, 60
Super-Goopy Glue, 79
Suzanna Socked Me Sunday, 121

There Is a Thing, 119
Throckmorton Thratte, 94
Today Is a Day to Crow About, 73
Today Is Very Boring, 96

Unassuming Owl, An, 23
Uncanny Colleen, 95
Underwater Wibbles, The, 16

We Each Wore Half a Horse, 67
We Heard Wally Wail, 42
What Nerve You've Got, Minerva Mott!, 43
When Dracula Went to the Blood Bank, 114
When Tillie Ate the Chili, 88
When Young, the Slyne, 115
Wolf Is at the Laundromat, A, 30

You Need to Have an Iron Rear, 15
Yubbazubbies, 68

Zany Zapper Zockke, 150
Zoosher, The, 122

Index to First Lines

A cow's outside is mainly hide, 51
A wolf is at the Laundromat, 30
Ah! A monster's lot is merry, 34
Ah! Welcome to my chamber, 140
Alligators are unfriendly, 14
An unassuming owl, 23

Baloney Belly Billy, 134
Be glad your nose is on your face, 64
Beneath a bush, the Zoosher lies, 122
Boing! Boing! Squeak!, 126
Bowen Ounce and Owen Bounce, 47
Bulgy Bunne (the wonder builder), 56

Come see the thing that Dad has caught—, 135
Consider the calamity, 108

Dauntless Dimble was the bravest, 70
Do oysters sneeze beneath the seas, 20

Eggs!, 104
Euphonica Jarre has a voice that's bizarre, 26
Every day, at ten past noon, 76

Granny Grizer, greedy miser, 32
Griselda Gratz kept sixty cats, 98

Henrietta Snetter knit a sweater in the night, 50
Homework! Oh, homework!, 54

I am a paramecium, 100
I am Ebenezer Bleezer, 48
I am falling off a mountain, 149
I am flying! I am flying!, 90
I am running in a circle, 18
I am standing by this lamppost, 38
I am the Flotz, I gobble dots, 52
I found a four-leaf clover, 74
I praise the hippopotamus, 131
I spied my shadow slinking, 72
I wonder why Dad is so thoroughly mad, 11
I'd never dine on dinosaurs, 146
I'd never eat a beet, because, 124
I'm a basic boneless chicken, 116

I'm an alley cat with one life left, 82
I'm bold, I'm brave, I know no fear, 133
I'm disgusted with my brother, 128
I'm Drumpp, the grump of the garbage dump, 12
I'm in a rotten mood today, 142
I'm thankful for my baseball bat, 28
I'm the single most wonderful person I know, 137
In the middle of a lily, 25
Its fangs were red with bloody gore, 22
I've got an incredible headache, 46
I've got an itch, a wretched itch, 24

Jellyfish stew, 8

Lavinia Nink lives serenely, 130
Louder than a clap of thunder, 36

Ma! Don't throw that shirt out, 120
Meet the lazy Nothing-Doings, 136
Michael built a bicycle, 102
Miraculous Mortimer (Master Magician), 139
My baby brother is so small, 61
My brother's head should be replaced, 101
My dog, he is an ugly dog, 62
My mother says I'm sickening, 112
My sister is a sissy, 138
"My stomach's full of butterflies!" 129

New York is in North Carolina, 78
Nine mice on tiny tricycles, 9
No, I won't turn orange, 31

Oh, Mabel, remarkable Mabel, 21
Oh, Teddy Bear, dear Teddy, 110

Permit me to present to you, 79

Serving supper, Sidney Snickke, 148
Sir Blushington Bloone is a knight of the court, 86
Something silky, scarcely there, 143
Stringbean Small was tall and trim, 60
Suzanna socked me Sunday, 121